11.00

D1600872

Queueing theory in OR

Queueing theory in OR

E. PAGE, B.Sc., Ph.D.

Lecturer, Sub-Department of
Operational Research, The
University, Hull

Crane Russak & Company, Inc.

New York

151685

658.4
P 132

Published in the United States by
Crane Russak & Company, Inc.
52 Vanderbilt Avenue,
New York, N.Y. 10017

First published 1972

© E. Page 1972

All rights reserved by
Butterworth & Co. (Publishers) Ltd., London

Library of Congress Catalog Number 72 – 79456

ISBN-0-8448 – 0016 – 3

Printed in Hungary

Preface

The aim of this book is to enable the operational research practitioner to obtain answers to queueing problems speedily by use of the theoretical or numerical results provided, and to give the student of operational research an introduction to the main areas of applied queueing theory.

The level of mathematics required is kept to that of the first year of a science degree. Theory is developed and numerical results given for queues which can be considered as extremes of those which occur in practice. Queues of a more general form are then considered. In cases where the mathematical development is difficult approximations are given and comparisons made between them and exact results. Problems are given as exercises for the readers at the end of all chapters except 8 and 9. The topics in these two chapters, queues with arrivals dependent on queue size, and priority queues, are more specialised than the others, and the variety of such queues is wider. The aim is to enable the reader to adapt the models given in these chapters to his own particular problem rather than to cover the whole range of such problems.

A glossary of terms used is given for those readers using the book as a reference.

I would like to thank Alun Davies of G.K.N. for his encouragement in the preparation of the book and Mrs. Caroline Everett for her typing of the manuscript.

Contents

TABLES

Contents

CHAPTER 1

Introduction

1.1. QUEUES IN INDUSTRY

Most industrial production processes have production cycles which are variable in their duration from one cycle to the next. While it may be possible to predict some of the variability there is usually some inherent variability which is unpredictable.

Since all machines require attention at some point in their production cycle, such as being supplied with raw material at the start, or despatch of their product at the finish, the call for the facilities meeting these needs is unpredictable.

When such variability occurs in a batch of several machines performing the same operation it is possible the calls on the services of the facilities may temporarily exceed the facilities available. At such times there will be a delay to one or more of the machines, usually costly because of the resulting loss in output, or delay in delivery of the product to a customer. Supplying facilities, be they men or equipment or both, to meet the requirements of the machines can also be costly. The determination of the number of facilities required to keep a batch of machines in economic operation is the problem facing the management in such a situation.

9

There is a close parallel between such industrial situations and the queues of customers in a shop or bank. Both situations have 'customers' requiring the attention of a 'server'. The customer in the shop requires the server to supply him with the goods he requires, the customer in the bank requires the teller to cash his cheque. The customer in the industrial situation is the machine, the server the man or machine providing the service of supplying raw material in one case and removing the finished product in the other. Because of the parallel between the situations they can both be considered as queues. There are many examples of this type of queueing situation in industry.

Ships arriving at a port can be considered as customers requiring the service of loading or unloading, the service being performed by the cranes at the berth occupied by the ship.

The arrival of ships is not always exactly predictable because of weather conditions on the voyage to the port. This may result in more ships requiring berths at some point in time than there are berths available at the port. It is costly to have ships waiting for berths, and also costly to invest in extra berths at a port. A decision has to be taken on the number of berths which will provide the most economic running of the port for the level and fluctuation in traffic it expects to receive. An exactly parallel situation occurs at airports, as aircraft can be ahead of schedule or delayed, resulting in queues of aircraft waiting for runways clear for them to land. The customers are the aircraft, the servers the runway for their landing or takeoff.

1.2 THE ELEMENTS OF THE QUEUEING SITUATION

The existence of a customer–server situation does not necessarily mean that queues of customers will develop. If there are sufficient servers available then customers will be served as soon as they require service. If the arrival of customers can be predicted, or controlled, then the service facilities can also be controlled to avoid any queues building up.

There are several factors which affect the time customers might be expected to wait, the frequency with which customers arrive at the system for service, the organisation of the service system, and the time it takes the server to serve the customer.

The frequency with which customers arrive obviously affects the likely waiting time of customers; the higher the arrival rate the longer the waiting time of a customer is likely to be. In the cases where there is some degree of uncertainty about the arrival time of customers, this uncertainty must be measured before it is possible to develop any results about waiting times of customers.

The most convenient way of measuring this uncertainty is to look at the intervals between successive customers arriving at the service system. The distribution of these intervals is called the *inter arrival distribution*, or sometimes more shortly the arrival distribution.

The organisation of the service system is the easiest way of controlling a queueing situation which may get a build up of customers. Most of the work on queues considers single queues which may be served by one or more servers, each customer requiring the full attention of one server during the time he is being served. In this simple situation the organisation of the service system can be described by the number of servers available to serve the customers. In many practical problems this number of servers will be varied deliberately, bringing in extra servers to serve a sudden rush of customers and then taking them off on to other work when the rush has been served. The organisation of such systems will be mentioned in a later chapter, but the bulk of the work will deal with systems having a constant number of servers available at all times.

The time taken to serve customers obviously has an effect on the length of queues that may form. A system with sufficient servers to meet the average rate of arrival of customers may still have queues forming if the service times are sufficiently variable. Periods when the service rate is temporarily slower than the arrival rate will have queues forming. The average service time, or service rate, is not sufficient to determine what will happen to the system in this situation. The distribution of service times must be known before a full study can be made.

The factors mentioned above are relevant in the calculation of the size of queues that form in a queueing system. These are not sufficient, however, to describe exactly what happens to each individual customer. In situations where a queue of several customers has been formed there must be some way of deciding which customer is to be served next. The rules determining this are called the *queue discipline*. The commonest form of queue discipline is first come, first served. This discipline will be assumed throughout except for a chapter on alternative disciplines.

1.3 MEASURES OF INTEREST IN A QUEUEING SYSTEM

A queueing system can be considered from three viewpoints, the customer's, the server's, or the organiser's of the service system. The customer usually would like to find a server free to serve him immediately on his arrival. This is not always possible, so the frequency with which customers have to wait is a measure of interest to customers. If a customer has to wait, the length of time he has to wait before he can be served will be important. This time will be different for each customer, and so is expressed statistically as a distribution of customer waiting time. The frequency with which customers have to wait is expressed as a fraction, or percentage, of the total number of customers. These are the two measures which will usually be calculated with reference to the customers.

The server will be interested in the length of time the server has to work without a break and the proportion of time on average he or she will be serving customers. The time a server is continuously busy serving customers without a break is called a *busy period*. The busy period will commence when the server starts work on a customer who has just arrived and will finish when the server completes the service of the same or a subsequent customer to find no other customer requiring service. At the end of a busy period, the server will be free until required to serve another customer on his arrival. These periods are sometimes called idle periods. The server's time alternates between busy and idle periods, both of which are variable in duration. The distribution of the length of each of these periods will be calculated with reference to the servers. The organisers of the service system will usually have to balance the previous viewpoints on either economic or intuitive bases.

Customer waiting time is usually unproductive, so if the customers are employed by the organisers of the service system this is a direct cost to the organisers. If the customers are not employed by the organisers they may not wait until servers become free if the waiting time is too long, but go elsewhere for service. The resulting loss of customers could result in an indirect cost due to loss of profit in the service system. On the other hand providing servers to decrease the waiting time is costly.

Somewhere between the situation of a few servers and long customer waiting times and the situation of many servers and low customer waiting time there is a system which will give a smaller running cost than any of the others. From the viewpoint of the organisers of the service system, both customers and servers are important and economic factors have to be considered in addition to those already mentioned for the customers and servers separately. The economic factors will be covered in chapters where results have been obtained for the statistical measures on customers and servers.

CHAPTER 2

Introduction to the Study of Queues

2.1 D. G. KENDALL'S NOTATION FOR QUEUEING SYSTEMS

One of the first problems in making a general study of queues is to obtain a system of classification which will cover a wide range of queueing situations. D. G. Kendall[1] proposed a notation which is now in common use. This caters for a single queueing system, i.e. one at which customers require a single service before departure from the system. It does not cater for customers requiring service from several service points in sequence. The factors determining the behaviour of such a system are:

1. The customer arrivals
2. The service times of customers
3. The service system

The customer arrivals and the service times are expressed as statistical distributions. The service system can be described by the number of servers in the system and the queue discipline. The queue discipline can be taken as first come, first served in many cases. This assumption will be made throughout this book unless specifically stated otherwise. The queueing system can now be described by the inter arrival distribution of customers, the distribution of service times, and the number of servers in the system. Kendall assigned a letter to each of several distributions and was then able to describe a queueing system by a three part code consisting of letter/letter/number. The first letter specifies the arrival distribution, the second letter specifies the service time distribution and the number specifies the number of servers.

The letters Kendall assigned to distributions are:

2.1.1 *M*—The Negative Exponential Distribution

The probability density function $f(x)$ of a variate x having a negative exponential distribution is:

$$f(x) = \frac{1}{A} e^{-x/A} \quad \text{for} \quad 0 \leqslant x < \infty \qquad (2.1)$$

The letter M was chosen to describe this distribution after A. Markov who did a lot of the early work on queues.

2.1.2 E_k—The Erlang Distribution

$$f(x) = \frac{b^{k+1}x^k e^{-bx}}{k!} \qquad 0 \leqslant x < \infty \qquad (2.2)$$

This is a more general distribution than the negative exponential because it requires two parameters, b and k to describe it, and was first used in the study of queues by A. K. Erlang.

2.1.3 *D*—The Deterministic Distribution

$$F(x) = \int_0^x f(u)\, du = \begin{cases} 0 & x < a \\ 1 & x \geqslant a \end{cases} \qquad (2.3)$$

The variate x in this distribution does not vary and takes the value a on all occasions. It is a useful approximation for variates which have very little variation.

2.1.4 *G*—The General Distribution

This letter is used to cover cases where no assumption is made about
the form of the distribution function. The results of studies with this
assumption are universally applicable.

While other distributions are known and could be assumed for the
arrival or service time distributions the first three mentioned above are
the most tractable to theoretical treatment. For this reason they are the
only distributions which are generally assigned letters for Kendall's
classification system.

2.2 THE DESCRIPTION OF THE STATE
OF A QUEUE

At first sight it may seem that the state of a queue can be described by
the number of customers in it at any time. It will be shown that this is
not a sufficient description of the state of a queue for a detailed study
leading to the evaluation of customer waiting time or length of server
busy periods etc.

The state of queueing systems, whose arrivals and/or service times
are variable, are not precisely predictable at future points in time.
What can be measured is the probability of the queue being in a particular state at a future point in time. If these probabilities are known the
factors of interest, such as customer waiting time, busy periods, etc. can
be calculated.

The state of a queue at any time is then defined as the knowledge of
the queue required to enable the equations for the probabilities of the
state of the queue at future points in time to be obtained. The general
form of these equations are easily written down.

Let $P_t(s_1)$ = the probability of the queue is in state s_1 at time t.

Let $T_t(s_1, s_2, a)$ = the probability of moving from state s_1 to state s_2 in
an interval of length a time units beginning at time t.

Then the probability equations are:

$$P_{t+a}(s_2) = \sum_{\text{all states } s_1} P_t(s_1)\, T_t(s_1, s_2, a) \qquad (2.4)$$

These equations relate probabilities at time t with probabilities at a time $t+a$. The number of customers in the queue is obviously one factor used to describe the state of the queue so the transition probabilities $T_t(s_1, s_2, a)$ will involve the likelihood of arrivals at and departures from the queue in the interval from t to $t+a$.

The number of arrivals in this interval will depend on the length of the interval and the time at which the last customer arrived before t, the start of the interval. This is most easily shown by considering the chance of an arrival in a very small interval, of length δt say, at a time T after the previous arrival. If $f(t)$ is the p.d.f. (probability density function) of the inter arrival intervals and $F(t) = \int_0^t f(u)\,du$ its cumulative function, let $p(T, \delta t)$ be the chance of an arrival in the small interval. Then

$$p(T, \delta t) = \frac{\{\text{the proportion of the distribution in the range } (T, T+\delta t)\}}{\{\text{the proportion of the distribution in excess of } T\}}$$

With δt being very small, the proportion of the distribution in the range $(T, T+\delta t)$ can be treated as a rectangle of width δt and height $f(T)$. The proportion in excess of T is $1 - F(T)$ giving

$$p(T, \delta t) = \frac{f(T)\,\delta t}{1 - F(T)} \qquad (2.5)$$

This is obviously a function of T and δt so the arrivals in an interval of length a will depend not only on a but also on the time at which the last customer arrived prior to the start of the interval. Similarly, the departures from a queueing system in an interval will depend on the length of the interval and the length of time any services in progress at the start of the interval had been going on.

The knowledge of the queue required to calculate $T_t(s_1, s_2, a)$ will include the time of arrival of the last customer prior to time t, and the time elapsed on any services in progress at time t.

For the purposes of a mathematical study of a queue the state of the queue at any time is then described by:

1. the length of the queue,
2. the time elaspsed since the last customer arrived, and
3. the duration of all services current at that time.

2.3 A SPECIAL DISTRIBUTION FUNCTION

The solution of equations 2.4 giving the probability of being in any state at any time has not so far been achieved except for particular distributions of arrivals and service times. Part of the difficulty in the general case is that knowledge of 2 and 3 above are necessary. These would not be necessary if $p(T, \delta t)$ in equation 2.5 did not depend on T. The necessary condition for this independence is:

$$p(T, \delta t) = k \, \delta t = \frac{f(T) \, \delta t}{1 - F(T)} \qquad (2.6)$$

that is

$$\frac{f(T)}{1 - F(T)} = k$$

or

$$\frac{dF(T)}{dT} = k(1 - F(T))$$

$$\frac{dF(T)}{1 - F(T)} = k \, dT$$

integrating, $-\log\left(1 - F(T)\right) = kT + c$

Since arrival intervals and service times are necessarily positive $F(0) = 0$

$$\therefore \quad c = 0$$
$$1 - F(T) = e^{-kT}$$
$$F(T) = 1 - e^{-kT}$$
$$f(T) = k \, e^{-kT} \qquad (2.7)$$

This is the negative exponential distribution, denoted by M in Kendall's notation. The average of the distribution is $1/k$, which is an average time. So k can be thought of as a 'rate', the rate of arrivals, or rate of service according to the distribution under consideration. Figure 2.1 shows the shape of the negative exponential distribution. The most likely values in the distribution are the smaller ones, the mode of the distribution occurring at 0. It is not likely that service times will have a distribution of this form in practice, though arrivals of customers at service points can quite often have distributions of this form.

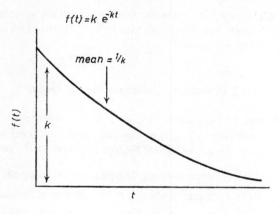

$f(t) = k\, e^{-kt}$

mean $= 1/k$

k

$f(t)$

t

Fig. 2.1

2.4 A SIMPLE QUEUE ($M/M/1$)

A queue with a negative exponential inter arrival distribution and negative exponential service time distribution with one server will now be considered in detail. In Kendall's notation this is described by the code $M/M/1$.

2.4.1 Definition of Parameters

Let $f(t)$ be the distribution function of the inter arrival times and a be the average interval between arrivals, then

$$f(t) = \lambda\, e^{-\lambda t} \tag{2.8}$$

where $\lambda =$ the arrival rate of customers $= 1/a$.

Let $g(u)$ be the distribution function of the service times and s be the average service time, then

$$g(u) = \mu\, e^{-\mu s} \tag{2.9}$$

where $\mu =$ the service rate $= 1/s$.

Let $P_t(i)$ = the probability there are i customers in the system at time t. Provided i is greater than zero, there will be $(i-1)$ customers waiting for service and one being served.

2.4.2 Probability Equations for the Queue

A small interval of time of length δt will be considered from t to $t+\delta t$. The probabilities $P_{t+\delta t}(i)$ at the end of the interval will be obtained in terms of the probabilities $P_t(i)$ at the start of the interval.

$P_{t+\delta t}(0) = P_t(0)\times$(chance nothing happens in the interval)

$+P_t(1)\times$(chance a service is completed in the interval)

$+P_t(2)\times$(chance 2 services are completed in the interval)

$+ \ldots$

From equations 2.8 and 2.9 the chance of a customer arriving in the interval is $\lambda\delta t$ for small values of δt, and similarly the chance the current service will finish in the interval is $\mu\delta t$.

The chance of two events happening in the interval, i.e. two arrivals, or two departures, or an arrival and a departure will be proportional to δt^2. It will later be seen that only the linear terms in δt are relevant, so multiple events can be neglected.

The chance nothing happens in the interval when there are no customers in the system at the start is the chance no customer arrives in the interval, i.e. $1-\lambda\,\delta t$, giving the form of equation:

$$P_{t+\delta t}(0) = P_t(0)(1-\lambda\,\delta t)+P_t(1)\,\mu\,\delta t+P_t(2)\times 0(\delta t^2)+ \ldots \quad (2.10)$$

The equations for the other probabilities at time $t+\delta t$ are all of the same form:

$P_{t+\delta t}(j) = P_t(j)\times$(chance of nothing happening in the interval)

$+P_t(j-1)\times$(chance of an arrival in the interval)

$+P_t(j+1)\times$(chance a service is completed in the interval)

$+$ terms involving multiple events in the interval.

This equation holds for $j = 1, 2, 3, \ldots, \infty$.

The chance nothing happens in the interval is now the chance of having neither an arrival, nor a service completed i.e. $(1-\lambda\,\delta t)(1-\mu\,\delta t)$, giving:

$$P_{t+\delta t}(j) = P_t(j)(1-\lambda\,\delta t)(1-\mu\,\delta t)+P_t(j-1)\,\lambda\,\delta t$$
$$+P_t(j+1)\mu\,\delta t+0(\delta t^2) \tag{2.11}$$
$$j = 1, 2, 3, \ldots, \infty.$$

These become on rearrangement:

$$\big(P_{t+\delta t}(0)-P_t(0)\big)/\delta t = \mu P_t(1)-\lambda P_t(0)+0(\delta t) \tag{2.12}$$
$$\big(P_{t+\delta t}(j)-P_t(j)\big)/\delta t = \lambda P_t(j-1)+\mu P_t(j+1)-(\lambda+\mu)\,P_t(j)+0(\delta t) \tag{2.13}$$
$$j = 1, 2, \ldots, \infty.$$

as δt tends to zero these become differential equations:

$$\frac{\mathrm{d}}{\mathrm{d}t}P_t(0) = \mu P_t(1)-\lambda P_t(0) \tag{2.14}$$

and

$$\frac{\mathrm{d}}{\mathrm{d}t}P_t(j) = \lambda P_t(j-1)+\mu P_t(j+1)-(\lambda+\mu)\,P_t(j) \tag{2.15}$$
$$j = 1, 2, \ldots, \infty.$$

Note: The terms involving δt and higher powers of δt have now dropped out, justifying the neglect of multiple events in the interval.

It can be shown that the general solution to these equations is:

$$P_t(j) = P_j+\sum_{k=1}^{\infty} A_{j,k}\,\mathrm{e}^{-c_k t} \tag{2.16}$$
$$j = 0, 1, 2, \ldots, \infty.$$

where P_j, $A_{j,k}$ are constants, and c_k are non-negative constants for the values of $A_{j,k}$ which are non-zero.

2.4.3 Steady State of a Queue

Usually the interest is in the behaviour of a queue over a long period of time, rather than in that for a short period after a particular point in time. It can be seen from the equation for the probabilities (equation 2.16) that the exponential terms will become negligible for large values of t. So eventually the probabilities will converge to the term independently of t, P_j.

Since the probabilities will then not change with time, the system is said to have reached a steady state. The system is of course 'steady' only in the sense that the probabilities do not change, not in the sense that the number of customers in the system does not alter. The behaviour of the queue over a long period of time will be dominated by the steady state probabilities, the effect of the initial transient exponential terms will be negligible in the long run.

The equations for the steady state probabilities are simpler than the time dependant probabilities. Since the steady state probabilities do not depend on time, the suffix t can be dropped from the probabilities so,

$P(j)$ = steady state probability there are j customers in the system

$$j = 0, 1, 2, \ldots, \infty \qquad (2.17)$$

also in the steady state $\qquad \dfrac{\mathrm{d}}{\mathrm{d}t} P_t(j) = 0 \qquad (2.18)$

$$j = 0,1,2, \ldots \ldots \infty$$

The equations 2.14 and 2.15 now become

$$\mu P(1) - \lambda P(0) = 0 \qquad (2.19)$$

and

$$\lambda P(j-1) + \mu P(j+1) - (\lambda + \mu) P(j) = 0 \qquad (2.20)$$

$$j = 1, 2, \ldots, \infty$$

by adding these equations together in sequence the equation

$$\mu P(j) = \lambda P(j-1)$$

$$j = 1, 2, \ldots, \infty$$

is obtained, giving

$$P(j) = \left(\frac{\lambda}{\mu}\right) P(j-1) = \left(\frac{\lambda}{\mu}\right)^J P(0) \qquad (2.21)$$

$$j = 1, 2, \ldots, \infty$$

The probabilities must sum to unity, so

$$\sum_{j=0}^{\infty} P(j) = 1 = \sum_{j=0}^{\infty} \left(\frac{\lambda}{\mu}\right)^J P(0) = \frac{P(0)}{(1 - (\lambda/\mu))} \quad \text{for} \quad \left(\frac{\lambda}{\mu}\right) < 1$$

i.e. $\qquad P(0) = 1 - \dfrac{\lambda}{\mu} \qquad (2.22)$

The condition for the convergence of the summation is that λ, the arrival rate of customers, must be less than μ, the service rate. If the arrival rate is greater than the service rate, obviously the service point is overloaded and in the long run queues will build up without limit. Under these conditions there is no steady state and hence no steady state probabilities. It should be noted that there is no steady state solution when the arrival rate is exactly equal to the service rate either. If the ratio λ/μ is denoted by ϱ then the probabilities are:

$$P(j) = (1-\varrho)\,\varrho^j \qquad (2.23)$$
$$j = 0, 1, 2, \ldots, \infty$$

2.4.4 Server Utilisation in the Steady State

The steady state probability $P(0)$ is the chance there are no customers in the system. The server is idle only when there are no customers in the system; whenever there is at least one customer in the system the server will be busy. The proportion of time the server will be busy, the server utilisation, is hence

$$1-P(0) = 1-(1-\varrho) = \varrho = \lambda/\mu$$

2.4.5 Distribution of Customer Waiting Time

The steady state probabilities are valid at any time at a service point which is in operation for a long period of time, after the initial transient terms become negligible. In particular they are valid at times when customers arrive. The chance a customer will arrive to find j customers already in the system is then $P(j)$ as given by equation 2.21. If there are no customers in the system when a customer arrives, the customer will not have to wait for service, hence

The chance a customer does not have to wait for service is

$$P(0) = 1-\varrho \qquad (2.24)$$

In all other cases the customer will have to wait. If a customer arrives to find j customers in the system he will have to wait until all these j customers have been served before his own service begins, (assuming a queue discipline of first come first served).

This waiting time can be considered as several sections, the first being the remainder of the service time of the customer being served on his arrival, the other sections being the individual service times of the other $j-1$ customers. If W_j is the waiting time of the customer, then

$$W_j = r_1 + s_2 + s_3 + \ldots + s_j \qquad (2.25)$$

where $r_1 = $ the remainder of service time of the customer being served on the arrival of the customer under consideration; and $s_2, s_3, \ldots, s_j$ are the individual service times of the other $j-1$ customers requiring service before the customer under consideration.

The distribution of the individual service times is known to be negative exponential. The only part of the waiting time whose distribution is not known is r_1, the remainder of the service time of the customer being served on the arrival of the customer under consideration. To obtain this distribution suppose the service started at time T before the arrival, so the total service time will be $T + r_1$ which has a negative exponential distribution. Let r_1 have a probability density function (p.d.f.) $g(r_1)$ then

$$g(r_1)\,dr_1 = \frac{\mu\,e^{-\mu(T+r_1)}}{[1-F(T)]}\,dr_1 \qquad (2.26)$$

where $F(T)$ is the cumulative p.d.f. of the negative exponential distribution, $F(T) = 1 - e^{-\mu T}$

hence
$$g(r_1)\,dr_1 = \frac{\mu e^{-\mu(T+r_1)}}{e^{-\mu T}}\,dr_1 = \mu e^{-\mu r_1}\,dr_1 \qquad (2.27)$$

That is, the remainder of the service time has exactly the same distribution as the full service time.

The distributions of the components of W_j are now known, assuming also that the individual service times are independent of each other, the distribution of W_j can be obtained. The proof of this is given in Hoel[2] and Weatherburn[3], the result will be quoted here without proof. The p.d.f. of $W_j = t$ say, is $f(t)$ where

$$f(t) = \frac{\mu^j t^{j-1} e^{-\mu t}}{(j-1)!} \qquad (2.28)$$

The chance of having to wait a time t will be the sum of the possibilities of having to wait a time t for any number of customers in the system on arrival. Let the p.d.f. be $W(t)$, then

$$W(t) = \sum_{j=1}^{\infty} P(j)\, W_j(t)$$

$$= (1-\varrho) \sum_{j=1}^{\infty} \frac{\varrho^j \mu^j t^{j-1}}{(j-1)!}\, e^{-\mu t}$$

$$= (1-\varrho)e^{-\mu t} \mu \varrho \sum_{j=1}^{\infty} \frac{(\varrho \mu t)^{j-1}}{(j-1)!}$$

$$= (1-\varrho)e^{-\mu t} \mu \varrho e^{\varrho \mu t}$$

$$= \mu \varrho (1-\varrho) e^{-\mu(1-\varrho)t} \qquad (2.29)$$

This function describes fully the waiting time a customer might expect in this queue, of particular interest is the average waiting time which is:

$$\text{Average waiting time} = \int_0^{\infty} t \cdot W(t)\, dt = \frac{\varrho}{(1-\varrho)\mu} = \frac{\varrho}{(1-\varrho)}\, s \qquad (2.30)$$

2.4.6 The Average Number of Customers in the System

This is easily obtained for the system in the steady state.

$$\text{Average number in the system} = \sum_{i=0}^{\infty} iP(i) = \sum_{i=0}^{\infty} i(1-\varrho)\varrho^i$$

$$= \varrho/(1-\varrho) \qquad (2.31)$$

Similarly the average number of customers queueing is

$$\sum_{i=1}^{\infty} (i-1)\, P(i) = \varrho^2/(1-\varrho) \qquad (2.32)$$

2.4.7 Server Utilisation

The proportion of time the server will be busy serving customers is called the server utilisation. Since the only time the server will not be serving customers is when there are no customers in the system, the server utilisation is (u say)

$$u = 1 - P(0)$$
$$= 1 - (1 - \varrho) = \varrho \qquad (2.33)$$

2.4.8 Busy Periods of the Server

A busy period is an interval during which the server is continually busy serving customers. In this particular queue a busy period will start at the arrival of a customer to the empty system and will finish as soon as the system becomes empty again. The distribution of the length of such intervals is obviously of interest to the server. The average length of busy periods can be found by considering the system for a long period of time T, say.

Since busy periods and idle periods alternate, in a long period of time there will be as many busy periods as idle periods.

The length of time the server will be busy is $(1 - P(0)) . T$, and the remaining time $P(0) . T$, is the length of time the server will be idle.

An idle period can only be terminated by the arrival of a customer. The idle period is hence the remainder of an arrival interval, the portion from the completion of the service of the last customer in one busy period to the arrival of the next to start the next busy period. By exactly similar arguments as for the derivation of equation 2.27 it can be shown that this distribution is the same as the complete inter arrival distribution $\lambda e^{-\lambda t}$. The average idle period is thus the same as the average arrival interval, $1/\lambda$.

In the long period of time, T, the number of idle intervals is (total idle time)/(average idle period), i.e.

$$P(0)T/(1/\lambda) = \lambda P(0)T$$

this will also be the average number of busy periods over the same length of time, i.e. (total busy time)/(average busy period) or

$(1 - P(0))T/$(average busy period). The equation of the average numbers gives:

$$\lambda P(0)T = (1 - P(0))T/\text{(average busy period)}$$

or

$$\text{average busy period} = (1 - P(0))/(\lambda P(0)) \qquad (2.34)$$

This equation will of course hold for any single server queueing system with random arrivals. In this particular case $P(0)$ is known and the formula reduces to

$$\text{average busy period} = \varrho/(\lambda(1 - \varrho)) \qquad (2.35)$$

The distribution of the busy period of the server can be calculated and is derived by Cox and Smith[4]: their result is quoted below.

The distribution function $f(t)$ of busy period t is

$$f(t) = \frac{e^{-(\lambda + \mu)t}}{t\varrho^{1/2}} J(v) \qquad (2.36)$$

where λ, μ, and ϱ are as defined above and

$$J(v) = \sum_{i=0}^{\infty} \frac{(\frac{1}{2}v)^{2i+1}}{i! \, (i+1)!}$$

$$v = 2t\mu\varrho^{1/2}$$

Example 2.1

A company owns a berth at a port, ships arrive for unloading at the berth on average every 12 h with a negative exponential distribution of intervals between ship arrivals. The ships are of a wide range of sizes resulting in a distribution of unloading time which is negative exponential in form. The average unloading time can be controlled by the type of unloading equipment installed at the berth.

The running costs of the berth are £10 000/m per day where m is the average unloading time at the berth, (in hours). Costs of delays to ships are £1 000 per ship day delay. What average unloading time should the equipment maintain for most economic running of the berth?

The running cost per day with unloading time m is £10 000/m
The delay cost per day with unloading time m is number of ships/day $\times$
average delay per ship $\times$ cost per ship day delay

$$= 2 \times \frac{m\varrho}{24(1-\varrho)} \times £1\ 000$$

$$\varrho = \frac{m}{l} = \frac{\text{average unloading time}}{\text{average arrival interval}} = \frac{m}{12}$$

Total cost $= 10\ 000/m + \dfrac{2m^2}{24(12-m)} \times 1\ 000$

The berth will be run most economically when this total cost is a minimum i.e. when

$$\frac{\mathrm{d}}{\mathrm{d}m}(\text{cost}) = 0$$

$$= \frac{-10\ 000}{m^2} + \frac{4\ 000m}{24(12-m)} + \frac{2\ 000m^2}{24(12-m)^2}$$

$$m^4 - 24m^3 + 120m^2 - 2\ 880m + 17\ 280 = 0$$

$m = 22 \cdot 817\ 936$, $6 \cdot 135\ 805$,   and two complex roots.

Only one of these four values is realistic i.e. $m = 6 \cdot 135\ 805$: the other real value would give an unloading time longer than the interval between ship arrivals.
The daily running cost with this unloading time is £1 630 and the delay cost is £535.
The average utilisation of the berth is $\varrho = m/12 = 0 \cdot 511\ 317$. The average delay per ship is $m\varrho/(1-\varrho) = 15 \cdot 33$ h.

2.5 THE MULTI-SERVER QUEUE $M/M/n$

One of the simplest methods of controlling queues in industry is to increase the number of servers available to deal with the customers. For example, most supermarkets have more than one check out point, banks more than one teller, and ports more than one berth. The alternatives are either to alter the service times or the arrivals of the customers.

The service time is usually difficult to change since this will mean either an alteration in the speed of the present system or a fundamental change in the method of service. In practice these possibilities will be considered and may result in several alternative modes of service. The queueing must then be studied for each alternative mode, and at this point of the study the service times of the system are not alterable.

The arrival of the customers in many industrial situations cannot be controlled to any extent. The arrivals of customers at a bank or supermarket are not controllable by their managements nor are the times of arrival of ships at most ports.

The only alternative left in many cases is to have a number of servers available to serve the customers. For the present it will be assumed that while serving a customer a server is unable to serve any other customer or do any other activity, and that there are n servers available.

Once again the arrivals pattern of customers and the distribution of service times will affect the queueing in the system and the case considered first is that in which both these are of the negative exponential form.

2.5.1 Mathematical Development for the Queue $M/M/n$

As for the single server queue the equations for the probabilities of there being any number of customers in the system at any time can be written down.

Let

$P_t(j)$ = the chance there are j customers in the system at time t

λ = the arrival rate of customers to the system

  = $1/a$

a = the average arrival interval

μ = the average service rate of service of a customer

  = $1/s$

s = the average service time of a customer

As shown previously the chance an arrival will occur in a small interval of length δt is $\lambda\, \delta t$ for the negative exponential distribution, and the chance of a service being completed in the same interval is $\mu\, \delta t$.

The equations for the probabilities at time $t+\delta t$ in terms of the probabilities at time t are hence:

$$P_{t+\delta t}(0) = P_t(0)(1-\lambda\,\delta t)+P_t(1)\mu\,\delta t$$
$$P_{t+\delta t}(1) = P_t(1)(1-\lambda\,\delta t)(1-\mu\,\delta t)+P_t(0)\lambda\,\delta t$$
$$+P_t(2)\,2\mu\,\delta t(1-\mu\,\delta t)$$
$$P_{t+\delta t}(j) = P_t(j)(1-\lambda\,\delta t)(1-\mu\,\delta t)^j+P_t(j-1)\lambda\,\delta t.$$
$$\times(1-\mu\,\delta t)^{j-1}+P_t(j+1)(j+1)\,\mu\,\delta t(1-\mu\,\delta t)^j$$
$$j \leqslant n$$
$$P_{t+\delta t}(j) = P_t(j)(1-\lambda\,\delta t)(1-\mu\,\delta t)^n+P_t(j-1)\lambda\,\delta t$$
$$\times(1-\mu\,\delta t)^n+P_t(j+1)\,n\mu\,\delta t(1-\mu\,\delta t)^{n-1}$$
$$j \geqslant n$$

which reduce to

$$P_{t+\delta t}(0) = P_t(0)(1-\lambda\,\delta t)+P_t(1)\mu\,\delta t$$
$$P_{t+\delta t}(1) = P_t(1)\big(1-(\lambda+\mu)\,\delta t+0(\delta t^2)\big)+P_t(0)\lambda\,\delta t$$
$$+P_t(2)\big(2\mu\,\delta t-0(\delta t^2)\big)$$
$$P_{t+\delta t}(j) = P_t(j)\big(1-(1+j\mu)\,\delta t+0(\delta t^2)\big)+P_t(j-1)$$
$$\times\big(\lambda\,\delta t-0(\delta t^2)\big)+P_t(j+1)\big((j+1)\mu\,\delta t-0(\delta t^2)\big)$$
$$j < n$$
$$P_{t+\delta t}(j) = P_t(j)\big(1-(\lambda+n\mu)\,\delta t+0(\delta t^2)\big)+P_t(j-1)$$
$$\times\big(\lambda\,\delta t-0(\delta t^2)\big)+P_t(j+1)\big(n\mu\,\delta t-0(\delta t^2)\big)$$
$$j \geqslant n \tag{2.37}$$

rearrangement and division by δt gives

$$(P_{t+\delta t}(0)-P_t(0))/\delta t = \mu P_t(1)-\lambda P_t(0)$$
$$(P_{t+\delta t}(1)-P_t(1))/\delta t = \lambda P_t(0)+2\mu P_t(2)-(\lambda+\mu)P_t(1)+0(\delta t)$$
$$(P_{t+\delta t}(j)-P_t(j))/\delta t = \lambda P_t(j-1)+(j+1)\mu P_t(j+1)$$
$$-(\lambda+j\mu)P_t(j)+0(\delta t)$$
$$j < n$$
$$(P_{t+\delta t}(j)-P_t(j))/\delta t = \lambda P_t(j-1)+n\mu P_t(j+1)$$
$$-(\lambda+n\mu)P_t(j)+0(\delta t)$$
$$j \geqslant n \tag{2.38}$$

As $\delta t \to 0$ the left hand sides become the differentials of the probabilities with respect to time and the terms of the order of δt on the right hand side will become negligible, giving:

$$\frac{\mathrm{d}}{\mathrm{d}t} P_t(0) = \mu P_t(1) - \lambda P_t(0)$$

$$\frac{\mathrm{d}}{\mathrm{d}t} P_t(j) = \lambda P_t(j-1) + (j+1)\,\mu P_t(j+1) - (\lambda + j\mu)\,P_t(j)$$

$j < n$

$$\frac{\mathrm{d}}{\mathrm{d}t} P_t(j) = \lambda P_t(j-1) + n\mu P_t(j+1) - (\lambda + n\mu)\,P_t(j)$$

$j \geqslant n$ (2.39)

The solutions to these equations for any initial probabilities after a transition period settle down to steady values which do not change with time. Since the interest is usually in the behaviour of the system over a long period of time these steady state probabilities are the ones required. The differentials are all zero when the steady state is reached which gives a simplified set of equations for these probabilities. The suffix t can also be dropped as the probabilities will not change with time, giving:

$P(j) =$ the steady state probability of there being j customers in the system.

$$\lambda P(0) = \mu P(1)$$

$$(\lambda + j\mu)\,P(j) = \lambda P(j-1) + (j+1)\,\mu P(j+1) \qquad j < n$$

$$(\lambda + n\mu)\,P(j) = \lambda P(j-1) + n\mu P(j+1) \qquad\qquad j \geqslant n \quad (2.40)$$

Taking these equations in turn and adding to the previous equations gives

$$P(1) \quad = \frac{\lambda}{\mu} P(0) = \varrho P(0) \quad \text{where} \quad \varrho = \lambda/\mu$$

$$P(j+1) = \frac{\lambda}{(j+1)\mu} P(j) = \frac{\varrho}{(j+1)} P(j) = \frac{\varrho^j}{(j+1)!} P(0), \qquad j < n$$

$$P(j+1) = \frac{\lambda}{n\mu} P(j) = \frac{\varrho}{n} P(j)$$

$$= \left(\frac{\varrho}{n}\right)^{j-n} \frac{\varrho^n}{n!} P(0) \qquad j \geqslant n \qquad (2.41)$$

Since the probabilities sum to unity

$$\sum_{j=0}^{\infty} P(j) = P(0) \left\{ 1 + \varrho + \frac{\varrho^2_{,}}{2!} + \ldots + \frac{\varrho^n}{n!} \left(1 + \frac{\varrho}{n} + \left(\frac{\varrho}{n}\right)^2 \right. \right.$$

$$\left. \left. + \left(\frac{\varrho}{n}\right)^3 + \ldots \right) \right\} = 1$$

$$P(0) \left\{ 1 + \varrho + \frac{\varrho^2}{2!} + \ldots + \frac{\varrho^n}{n!} \; \frac{1}{(1 - \varrho/n)} \right\} = 1$$

provided $\varrho/n < 1$.

$$P(0) = \left\{ 1 + \varrho + \frac{\varrho^2}{2!} + \frac{\varrho^3}{3!} + \frac{\varrho^{n-1}}{(n-1)!} + \frac{\varrho^n}{n! \, (1 - \varrho/n)} \right\}^{-1} \qquad (2.42)$$

Some factors can be calculated directly.

The average number of customers in the system

$$= \sum_{j=0}^{\infty} j P(j) = \varrho P(0) \left\{ 1 + \varrho + \frac{\varrho^2}{2!} + \ldots + \frac{\varrho^{n-2}}{(n-2)!} + \frac{\varrho^{n-1}}{n!} \right.$$

$$\left. \left\{ \frac{(n-1)}{(1 - \varrho/n)} + \frac{1}{(1 - \varrho/n)^2} \right\} \right\} \qquad (2.43)$$

The average number of customers in the queue

$$= \sum_{j=n}^{\infty} (j - n) \, P(j)$$

$$= P(0) \, \frac{\varrho^n}{n!} \, \frac{(\varrho/n)}{(1 - \varrho/n)^2} \qquad (2.44)$$

The Distribution of Waiting Time

The queue discipline of first come first served will be observed as it is the commonest form. A customer will have to wait until all the customers in the system on his arrival have started service before he can be served. Obviously a customer will not have to wait at all if there are less than n customers in the system on his arrival. Since the steady state probabilities are valid at any point in time they are valid in particular at points of arrival of customers, and give the probability a customer will find any particular number of customers in the system.

The chance a customer does not have to wait is hence

$$P(0)+P(1)+ \ldots +P(n-1) = P(0)\left\{1+\varrho+ \ldots +\frac{\varrho^{n-1}}{(n-1)!}\right\} \quad (2.45)$$

A customer who has to wait will have more than n customers in the system on his arrival. All n servers will be busy in this circumstance and will continue to be busy at least until the present customer begins being served; or as soon as a server finishes serving one customer he will begin service of one of the customers still waiting.

If the customer found $n+j$ customers in the system on his arrival then $j+1$ these must complete their service before a server is free to serve the customer in question.

His waiting time can be divided into intervals between successive customers leaving the system, it being terminated when the $(j+1)$th customer departs. If the distribution of these intervals can be found then the waiting time distribution can be built up from it. This distribution is derived below.

Distribution of the interval between successive departures from the system when all n servers are busy

Consider a point in time at which a customer service is completed. The distribution function, $f(t)$, of the time t it takes the server of that customer to complete the service of the next customer is the service time distribution function:

$$f(t) = \mu e^{-\mu t}$$

The other $(n-1)$ servers will have partially completed their services and only have some remainder of these services to be completed. It has been shown previously (equation 2.27) that the distribution of each of these remainders is exactly the same as the full service time distribution for this particular form of distribution.

So if $t_r = $ the remaining service time of a customer at any point after commencement

then $f(t_r) = \mu e^{-\mu t_r}$

Each of the $n-1$ remainders of service on the other servers will have this distribution. The distribution $(g(t)$, say$)$ of the interval between successive departures (t) is then

$$g(t) = nf(t)\,[1 - F(t)]^{n-1}$$
$$= n\mu e^{-\mu t}\, e^{-\mu t(n-1)}$$
$$= n\mu e^{-n\mu t} \tag{2.46}$$

The distribution is still of the negative exponential form. Its average rate is n times that of the individual servers as one might expect.

A customer waiting j such intervals will have a distribution $W_j(t)$ for waiting time t as shown in equation 2.28.

$$W_j(t) = (n\mu)^j\, \frac{t^{j-1}\, e^{-n\mu t}}{(j-1)!} \tag{2.47}$$

The distribution of customer waiting time is now obtainable from the probabilities of the number of customers ahead of the arriving customer and the conditional distribution of waiting time above equation 2.47. If the waiting time distribution is defined as $W(t)$ then

$$W(t) = \sum_{j=0}^{\infty} P(n+j)\, W_{j+1}(t)$$

$$= \sum_{j=0}^{\infty} \frac{\varrho^n}{n!}\, P(0) \left(\frac{\varrho}{n}\right)^j (n\mu)^{j+1}\, \frac{t^j}{j!}\, e^{-n\mu t}$$

$$= \frac{\varrho^n}{n!}\, P(0) e^{-n\mu t}\, n\mu \sum_{j=0}^{\infty} \left(\frac{\varrho}{n}\, n\mu t\right)^j \Big/ j!$$

$$= \frac{\varrho^n}{n!}\, P(0) e^{-n\mu t}\, n\mu e^{\lambda t}$$

$$= \frac{\varrho^n}{n!}\, P(0) n\mu e^{-(n\mu - \lambda)t} \tag{2.48}$$

The waiting time distribution is also of the negative exponential form. Its average by integration is:

$$\text{average waiting time} = \frac{1}{n\mu}\, \frac{\varrho^n}{n!}\, \frac{P(0)}{(1 - \varrho/n)^2} \tag{2.49}$$

The average number of servers busy

$$= 0P(0)+1P(1)+ \ldots +(n-1)P(n-1)+n\{P(n)+P(n+1)+ \ldots\}$$

on reduction

$$= \varrho$$

hence the server utilisation $= \varrho/n$ (2.50)

2.5.2 Busy Periods of Servers

Busy periods can now be considered for individual servers or for the system as a whole. Considering the system as a whole first it will be empty only when there are no customers in the system, and will be busy at other times. The average length of busy period for the system can be derived by an exactly parallel argument to that for the single server queue given in equation 2.35.

Average busy period for the system $= (1-P(0))/(\lambda P(0))$ (2.51)

When individual servers are considered, they will alternate between busy periods and idle periods. The proportion of time spent in each period on average can be found from the utilisation, the number of each type of period in a long interval of time will be equal so once either average duration is known the other can be found using this equality.

The average idle interval is easiest to determine. Consider a server just having completed serving a customer. This server will commence an idle period if at this point there are less than n customers remaining in the system, let $j(< n)$ be this number of customers. At this point $(n-j)$ servers will be idle. Assuming they return to service in the order in which they become idle, the current server will return for service when the $(n-j)$th customer arrives from the current time. This interval will on average be $(n-j)/\lambda$. Hence

$\bar{I}(j) =$ the average idle interval of a server finding j customers in the system at commencement of the idle period

$$= (n-j)/\lambda$$

The conditional probability of finding j customers in the system at the start of an idle period is $a(j)$ where

$$a(j) = P(j)\Big/\sum_{j=1}^{n-1} P(j)$$

The average idle period $\bar{I}$ is hence

$$\bar{I} = \sum_{j=0}^{n-1} a(j)\cdot(n-j)/\lambda$$

$$= \left\{\sum_{j=0}^{n-1} (n-j)\,\varrho^j/j\right\}\Big/\left\{\lambda\sum_{j=0}^{n-1} \varrho^j/j!\right\} \tag{2.52}$$

Using the equality of number of busy and idle periods the average busy period $\bar{B}$ is given by:

$$(1-\varrho/n)/\bar{I} = (\varrho/n)/\bar{B}$$
$$\bar{B} = \varrho\bar{I}/(n-\varrho) \tag{2.53}$$

It has been necessary in the calculation of this average to assume a 'server discipline' of first idle first back for service. This is a reasonable assumption for queues with human servers but for queues with machines as servers other disciplines may be used.

2.5.3 Numerical Results for the Queue M/M/n

It is now possible to tabulate some of the more common factors of interest in a queue such as:

Chance of a customer not having to wait for service,
The average waiting time of a customer,
The average busy period of a server.

The tables giving these results are collected together at the end of the book for easy reference in use. These cover the range of utilisation from 0·1 to 0·9 in steps of 0·1 and each number of servers from 2 to 10. Table A.1 gives the average waiting time over all customers, Table A.6 gives the chance a customer does not have to wait, and Table A.10 the average busy period of individual servers.

Example 2.2

A supermarket finds customers arrive at the check outs on average every six seconds with a negative exponential distribution. The service time takes twenty seconds on average, again with a negative exponential distribution. If it costs 100 p an hour to provide a single check out point and the cost of customer waiting time is equally valuable, how many check out points should there be?

The hourly cost of running the supermarket with n check outs will be:

100 p$\times n$+100 p$\times$average number of customers/h$\times$average waiting time per customer in h = $100\times(n+600\times$Av. Wait)p

from the tables,

$$\varrho = \frac{\text{Av. service time}}{\text{Av. arrival interval}} = \frac{20}{6} = 3\frac{1}{3}$$

n must be at least 4 for steady state solutions to be obtained, $(\varrho/n < 1)$. If values of n from 4 to 8 are considered, the results are given in Table 2.1.

Table 2.1

n	utilisation ϱ/n	average wait* in units of service time	hourly cost (£)
4	0·833 3	1·030 4 (0·986 6)	7·44
5	0·666 7	0·195 8 (0·196 0)	5·65
6	0·555 6	0·054 6 (0·055 6)	6·18
7	0·476 2	0·016 3 (0·016 7)	7·05
8	0·4167	0·004 9 (0·004 9)	8·02

* The figures for average waiting time were obtained from the tables by linear interpolation on the log of the waiting time and then taking the anti log of the value. The figures in brackets are the exact values of waiting time calculated using the formula.

The cost is least when $n = 5$ so five check out points should be provided. With this number of check outs,

The average waiting time is $0·1958\times10 = 3·9$ s.

The chance a customer does not have to wait is, by linear interpolation in the tables, 66·94%.

The average busy period for a server is 29·7 s.

The average idle period for a server is 14·9 s.

Example 2.3

A general stores in a factory has three separate counters for stationery, electrical parts, and mechanical parts respectively. One storeman is available at each counter to serve customers requiring the appropriate material. The service times of all three storemen have the same distribution, negative exponential with a mean of 15 s. The arrivals at each counter are random with averages of 20 s, 18 s and 30 s respectively.

By how much would the average waiting time over all customers drop if each counter was able to deal with any type of material?

The present method of operation is as three separate queues, each with a single server. Using the formulae for $M/M/1$ the waiting times for each of these can be found.

Average waiting time at stationery counter $= s \cdot \dfrac{\varrho}{(1-\varrho)}$

where s = average service time = 15 s.

$$\varrho = \frac{\text{service time}}{\text{arrival interval}} = \frac{15}{20} = 0.75$$

$$\text{hence average wait} = 15 \times \frac{0.75}{0.25} = 45 \text{ s.}$$

Similarly,

Average wait at electrical counter $= 15 \times \dfrac{\frac{5}{6}}{\frac{1}{6}} = 75$ s.

Average wait at mechanical counter $= 15 \times \dfrac{\frac{1}{2}}{\frac{1}{2}} = 15$ s.

Average wait over all customers

$\qquad$ = proportion of all customers requiring stationery
$\qquad$ $\times$ average wait at stationery counter
$\qquad$ + proportion of all customers requiring electrical parts
$\qquad$ $\times$ average wait at electrical counter
$\qquad$ + proportion of all customers requiring mechanical parts
$\qquad$ $\times$ average wait at mechanical counter.

The proportions can be found from the arrival rates, each minute

3 customers arrive at the stationery counter,
$\frac{10}{3}$ customers arrive at the electrical counter,

and 2 customers arrive at the mechanical counter,

the proportions are then $\dfrac{3}{(3+3\frac{1}{3}+2)}$, $\dfrac{\frac{10}{3}}{(3+3\frac{1}{3}+2)}$, $\dfrac{2}{(3+3\frac{1}{3}+2)}$ respectively, hence the average wait

$$= \frac{3}{8\frac{1}{3}}\times 45 + \frac{3\frac{1}{3}}{8\frac{1}{3}}\times 75 + \frac{2}{8\frac{1}{3}}\times 15 = \frac{1\,245}{25} = 49\cdot 8 \text{ s.}$$

When all counters can deal with any type of customer, the service time distributions are the same as the separate counters. The arrival distribution is still negative exponential with the combined rate of $8\frac{1}{3}$ customers per minute. The system is now a 3 server system with $\varrho = \dfrac{15\times 8\frac{1}{3}}{60}$

$= 125/60 = 2\frac{1}{12}$

The formula for average waiting time gives

Average waiting time for the combined system $= 0\cdot 5282\times 15 = 7\cdot 9$ s (Logarithmic interpolation in the tables gives the average waiting time as $0\cdot 5286\times 15$ s, which is in close agreement with the exact result).

By extending the three counters so each can deal with all types of material the average waiting time of customers has been greatly reduced, from 49·8 s to 7·9 s on average. This is what one would expect of course. The magnitude of the saving in average waiting time increases with the utilisation of the system.

2.6 PROBLEMS ON THE QUEUE $M/M/n$

1. Ships arrive at a port at a rate of one every 3 h, with a negative exponential distribution of inter arrival times. The time a ship occupies a berth for unloading and loading has a negative exponential distribution with an average of 12 h. If the average delay to ships waiting for berths is to be kept below 6 h, how many berths should there be at the port?

2. Customers arrive for service in a Poisson stream at a rate of one a minute. The service time has a negative exponential distribution with a mean of 0·9 min. The cost of making one server continuously available is £14 per week. The cost of keeping a customer waiting is $8\frac{1}{2}$ p per hour. How many servers should be made continuously available to minimise the total cost of servers and customer waiting time?

3. An engineering repair shop for a large company finds items requiring repair arrive at random with an average interval between calls of 20 min. The repair times are 40 min on average with a negative exponential distribution. Each call requires the service of one mechanic. How many mechanics are necessary to ensure that the average busy period of a mechanic does not exceed one hour and the average idle period of a mechanic is greater than 10 min?

4. Taxis arrive at random at a taxi rank on average every 2 min. If a taxi arrives to find no customers at the rank it will leave immediately to find customers at other ranks. Customers also arrive at random on average every 3 min. What proportion of taxis will leave the rank without a customer, and what is the average waiting time of customers at the rank?

5. Show that the average time in system of a customer in the single server queue $M/M/1$ with utilisation u and service time s is always less than the average time in system for a customer in the system $M/M/2$ with utilisation u and service time $2s$.

6. A petrol station has two pumps of each of two grades of petrol all being of the self service type. The filling time of each of the four pumps has a negative exponential distribution with an average of 2·5 min. The customer arrival intervals are also exponentially distributed with a average of 1·5 min for grade one petrol and 2·5 min for grade two petrol. What is the average waiting time of customers irrespective of the grade they require?

If the pumps are modified so each will provide either grade of petrol as required with the distribution of filling time being unaltered by how much will the waiting time be reduced?

7. Customers arrive at the check outs of a supermarket at random at the rate of three a minute. The service time of a customer is half a minute on average with a negative exponential distribution.

What is the least number of servers required to satisfy all three restraints under steady state conditions?

1. At least 90% of customers do not have to wait
2. The average idle time of servers must be greater than 5 min
3. The average waiting time of customers must be less than half the average service time.

CHAPTER 3

Queues with Constant Service Times and Random Arrivals of Customers

3.1 MATHEMATICAL DEVELOPMENT OF THE SINGLE SERVER QUEUE $M/D/1$

The previous chapter deals entirely with arrivals and service times having the negative exponential distribution. The assumption of this distribution applying to both arrivals and service is restrictive in practice, being most restrictive when applied to the service time distribution. Service times are not so variable in practice as this distribution. The coefficient of variation is defined as the standard deviation/mean and is a measure of the variability of a distribution. For a variable t, with distribution function $f(t)$,

$$\text{the Standard Deviation} = (E(t^2) - E(t)^2)^{1/2}.$$

$$\text{and the Mean} = E(t).$$

where
$$E(t^2) = \int t^2 f(t)\, dt$$
and
$$E(t) = \int t f(t)\, dt.$$

For the negative exponential distribution the coefficient of variation is $1 \cdot 0$. A service time which is constant for all customers will have a standard deviation of zero and hence a coefficient of variation of zero. The coefficients of variation of most distributions occuring in practical situations are usually between these two values. The study of these two extreme cases enables limits to be put on factors in the practical situation. The negative exponential assumption gives an overestimate to the queueing, and the constant assumption gives an underestimate. These limits may well be sufficiently close to enable the practical problem to be answered without any development of models which more closely match the actual distributions appearing in the practical case. Some practical problems do have very little variation in the service time, for example a berth unloading ships of the same size will produce a distribution of unloading time which is very nearly constant. Study of this model is useful then both as an approximation to many practical situations and in combination with the assumption of the negative exponential distribution provides limits on the queueing in many others.

3.1.1 Mathematical Approach to the Queue

The approach used in studying the previous case is no longer applicable because the chance of a service being completed in a small interval of time is no longer independent of the time elapsed since the start of service. With constant service time the point of completion is determined precisely immediately the service has started. The approach is modified by considering the queue system at points a service time apart. Any service begun at the first point will have finished by the second point and the customers left the system. Any service started during the interval will be unfinished at the second point. Departures from the system in the interval are now covered. Arrivals of customers to the system in the interval can be obtained by dividing the interval into the times between customer arrivals.

The interval is equal to the service time s; suppose n customers arrive in the interval.

Let r_1 = the remainder of the inter arrival interval current at the start of the interval.

t_2 = the arrival interval between the 1st and 2nd customer.

t_3 = the arrival interval between the 2nd and 3rd customer.

t_n = the arrival interval between the $(n-1)$th and nth customer.

v = the portion of the arrival interval current at the end of the interval which has elapsed at that time.

then $$s = r_1 + t_2 + t_3 + \ldots + t_n + v \qquad (3.1)$$

It has previously been shown that the remainder of the arrival interval r_1 will have the same distribution as a full arrival interval for the negative exponential distribution. The probability distribution of n such intervals taking a time u has also been shown to be:

$$f(u) = \lambda^n \frac{u^{n-1} e^{-\lambda u}}{(n-1)!}$$

The probability one arrival interval will exceed v is

$$\int_v^\infty \lambda e^{-\lambda t}\, dt = e^{-\lambda v}$$

The probability n arrivals occur in $s = u+v$ is

$$a(n) = \int_{u=0}^{u=s} f(u)\, e^{-\lambda v}\, du$$

since $v = s-u$

$$a(n) = \int_0^s f(u)\, e^{-\lambda(s-u)}\, du = \int_0^s \lambda^n \frac{u^{n-1}}{(n-1)!}\, e^{-\lambda u}\, e^{-\lambda(s-u)}\, du$$

$$= \frac{\lambda^n e^{-\lambda s}}{(n-1)!} \int_0^s u^{n-1}\, du = \frac{(\lambda s)^n}{n!}\, e^{-\lambda s} \qquad (3.2)$$

The number of arrivals, n, in the service time s has a Poisson distribution with a means λs, the average number of arrivals in a service time. This result is well known and changes in the system in a service time, of arrivals, and departures are now known.

The probabilities of the number of customers at the end of the interval can now be specified in terms of the probabilities at the start and the changes occurring during the interval.

Let

$P_t(n) =$ the probability there are n customers in the system at time t

$a(j) =$ the probability of j customers arriving in a service time, s

$\quad = \dfrac{(\lambda s)^n}{n!}\, e^{-\lambda s}$

then

$$P_{t+s}(0) = P_t(0)\,a(0) + P_t(1)\,a(0)$$

At the start of the interval there could have been no customers in the system, none arrive during the interval, leaving none at the end. Alternatively there could have been one customer in the system at the start, who will be being served at that time and so finish service and depart before the end of the interval, leaving no customers remaining from the start of the interval. No further customers arrive during the interval leaving no customers at the end.

If there had been two or more customers in the system at the start of the interval, the one being served at that time would have completed service and departed before the end leaving the other customer, or customers, still in the system at the end of the interval. Similarly the other probability equations can be written down:

$$P_{t+s}(1) = P_t(0)\,a(1) + P_t(1)\,a(1) + P_t(2)\,a(0)$$
$$P_{t+s}(j) = P_t(0)\,a(j) + P_t(1)\,a(j) + P_t(2)\,a(j-1) + P_t(3)\,a(j-2)$$
$$+ \ldots + P_t(r)\,a(j-r+1) + \ldots + P(j+1)\,a(0)$$
$$j = 2, 3, \ldots, \infty \qquad (3.3)$$

These equations will give the probabilities at any time given the initial state of the system. However the interest is usually in the states of the queue over a long period of time. The probabilities, as in the case of $M/M/n$, settle down to values which are not dependent on the initial conditions, a steady state solution. Once this steady state is reached the probabilities do not change with the value of t. The steady state solution can be found dropping the suffix t in the equations 3.3 and solving the resulting equations, which are:

$$P(0) = \{P(0) + P(1)\}\,a(0)$$
$$P(j) = (P(0) + P(1))\,a(j) + \sum_{r=2}^{r=j+1} P(r)\,a(j-r+1) \qquad (3.4)$$

By rearranging the equations the probabilities can be obtained in terms of $P(0)$

$$P(1) = P(0)\,[1 - a(0)]a/(0)$$
$$P(2) = [P(1)\,(1 - a(1)) - P(0)\,a(1)]/a(0) \quad \text{etc.}$$

Using the identity $\sum_{j=0}^{\infty} P(j) \equiv 1$ enables $P(0)$ to be calculated and hence by back substitution all the other probabilities. When the method is used numerically, rounding errors increase as the $P(j)$s are calculated for the higher values of j. This is because each estimate is the difference of terms divided by a figure less than 1, $(a(0))$. An alternative approach avoids this difficulty and is given below.

3.2 THE PROBABILITY GENERATING FUNCTION

Consider the function

$$F(x) = \sum_{j=0}^{\infty} x^j P(j) \tag{3.5}$$

Taking the equations 3.4, multiplying the equation with $P(j)$ on the left hand side by x^j for all values of j from 0 to ∞ and summing all equations, the equation below is obtained.

$$\sum_{j=0}^{\infty} x^j P(j) = (P(0)+P(1))\, a(0) + \sum_{j=1}^{\infty} x^j \left[(P(0)+P(1))\, a(j) \right.$$

$$\left. + \sum_{j=2}^{r=j+1} P(r)\, a(j-r+1) \right]$$

$$= (P(0)+P(1)) \sum_{j=0}^{\infty} x^j a(j) + \sum_{j=2}^{\infty} P(j) \sum_{k=0}^{\infty} x^{k+j-1} a(k)$$

Since $\sum_{j=0}^{\infty} x^j a(j) = \Sigma x^j \dfrac{\varrho^j}{j!}\, e^{-\varrho} = e^{\varrho x-\varrho}$, where $\varrho = \lambda s$, the equation reduces to

$$F(x) = [P(0)+P(1)]\, e^{\varrho(x-1)} + \sum_{j=2}^{\infty} P(j) x^{j-1} e^{\varrho x-\varrho}$$

$$F(x) e^{\varrho(1-x)} = P(0)+P(1) + \sum_{j=2}^{\infty} x^j P(j)/x$$

$$= P(0)+P(1) + [F(x)-xP(1)-P(0)]/x$$

$$F(x)\, [e^{\varrho(1-x)}-1/x] = P(0)\, (1-1/x)$$

$$F(x) = \frac{P(0)\, (x-1)}{x e^{\varrho(1-x)}-1} \tag{3.6}$$

when $x = 1$ $F(1) = \Sigma P(j) = 1$

the right hand side $= P(0) \lim_{x \to 1} \left[\dfrac{(x-1)}{xe^{\varrho(1-x)}-1} \right]$

when $x = 1$ both the numerator and denominator are zero. The value of the ratio is equal to the value of the ratio of the differentials of the numerator and denominator, (see Phillips[5] p. 107) giving

$$\lim_{x \to 1} \frac{x-1}{xe^{\varrho(1-x)}-1} = \lim_{x \to 1} \frac{1}{(1-\varrho x)e^{\varrho(1-x)}} = \frac{1}{1-\varrho}$$

hence $P(0)\dfrac{1}{1-\varrho} = 1$

$$P(0) = 1 - \varrho \tag{3.7}$$

The probabilities can now be found in turn by differentiating $F(x)$ and evaluating at $x = 0$, for,

$$\frac{d^n}{dx^n} F(x) = \frac{1}{n!} P(n) + \frac{x}{(n+1)!} P(n+1) + \text{higher powers of } x$$

$$\left. \frac{d^n}{dx^n} F(x) \right|_{x=0} = \frac{1}{n!} P(n) \tag{3.8}$$

The values of the individual probabilities are not usually of direct interest, but indirectly in that they are required for the calculation of such factors as the average number of customers in the queue, in the system, and the average waiting time of customers. These can be found in terms of the generating function $F(x)$, for example,

average number of customers in the system $= \displaystyle\sum_{j=0}^{\infty} jP(j)$

$$\left. \frac{d}{dx} F(x) \right|_{x=1} = \left. \frac{d}{dx} \left[\sum_{j=0}^{\infty} x^j P(j) \right] \right|_{x=1} = \left. \sum_{j=1}^{\infty} jx^{j-1} P(j) \right|_{x=1}$$

$$= \sum_{j=0}^{\infty} jP(j)$$

hence average number of customers in the system $= \left. \dfrac{d}{dx} F(x) \right|_{x=1}$

$= (1-\varrho) [xe^{\varrho(1-x)} - 1 - (x-1)(1-\varrho x)e^{\varrho(1-x)}]/(xe^{\varrho(1-x)} - 1)^2$ at $x = 1$

the numerator and denominator are both zero so the ratio of the first
non zero differentials must be used to obtain the value, giving

$$= (1-\varrho)\frac{\varrho(2-\varrho)}{2(1-\varrho)^2} = \frac{\varrho(2-\varrho)}{2(1-\varrho)} \tag{3.9}$$

Average number of customers in the queue $= \sum_{j=2}^{\infty} (j-1)P(j)$

$$= \sum_{j=1}^{\infty} jP(j) - \sum_{j=1}^{\infty} P(j)$$

$$= \frac{\varrho(2-\varrho)}{2(1-\varrho)} - (1-P(0)) = \frac{\varrho(2-\varrho)}{2(1-\varrho)} - \varrho = \frac{\varrho^2}{2(1-\varrho)} \tag{3.10}$$

The average waiting time of customers can be found by considering
the average waiting time of a customer arriving to find j customers in
the system and then averaging over all possible values of j.

A customer arriving to find j customers in the system, with a first
come first served queue discipline, will have to wait until these j customers have been served before he commences being served. This will
be the remaining part of the service of the customer being served on his
arrival and the complete service time of the other $(j-1)$ customers.
Since the service time is constant and the customer could arrive at any
time during a service with equal probability, the average of the remainder of the service in progress is $\bar{r}$ where

$$\bar{r} = \int_0^s rf(r)\,dr$$

where $f(r)$ is the distribution function of the remainder and $f(r) = \dfrac{1}{s}$

$$\bar{r} = \int_0^s \frac{r}{s}\,dr = \frac{s}{2} \tag{3.11}$$

The average waiting time is then $\bar{r}+(j-1)s = (j-\tfrac{1}{2})s$

The average waiting time for all customers

$$= \sum_{j=1}^{\infty} P(j) \left(j - \frac{1}{2} \right) s$$

$$= s \left[\sum_{j=1}^{\infty} jP(j) - \frac{1}{2} (1 - P(0)) \right]$$

$$= s \left[\frac{\varrho(2 - \varrho)}{2(1 - \varrho)} - \frac{1}{2} \varrho \right] = s \frac{\varrho}{2(1 - \varrho)} \tag{3.12}$$

The chance a customer does not have to wait is $P(0) = 1 - \varrho$

Factors concerning the server of the system can also be calculated. The utilisation of the server $= 1 - P(0) = \varrho$.

The average busy period of the server can be found by exactly the same argument as for the queue $M/M/1$ (equation 2.34) since the arrivals are still random, giving $\bar{B}$, the average busy period as:

$$\bar{B} = [1 - P(0)]/[\lambda P(0)]$$
$$= s/(1 - \varrho)$$

The distribution of the busy period can be found by considering the probabilities of the server having served n customers from the start of a busy period finding there are still j customers to be served. The derivation of the distribution is given in Tanner[6]; if $B(n)$ is the chance there are n customers served in a busy period,

then
$$B(n) = \frac{(n\varrho)^{n-1}}{n!} e^{-n\varrho} \tag{3.13}$$

This distribution is known as the Borel[7] distribution.

Since the service time is constant, busy periods can only take values which are multiples of the service time, s, and the probability the busy period will be of length ns is $B(n)$.

3.3 MULTI-SERVER QUEUES, $M/D/n$

The methods used for deriving results for the single server queue with constant service can be adapted for the study of multi-server queues with contant service time. Let

$P_t(j)$ = the probability there are j customers in the system at time t.
$a(i)$ = the chance i customers arrive in an interval equal to the service time, s,

as derived in equation 3. 2

$$a(k) = \frac{\varrho^{-k}}{k!} e^{-\varrho}$$

where
$$\varrho = \frac{\text{service time}}{\text{arrival interval}} = \lambda s$$

By considering the system at points in time a service time apart the probabilities $P_{t+s}(j)$ at time $t+s$ can be found in terms of events in the interval and the probabilities $P_t(j)$ at time t. Any customer being served at the start of the interval will have finished being served and left the system by the end of the interval. Any other customer will still be in the system at the end of the interval. The equations for the probabilities are hence:

$$P_{t+s}(0) = P_t(0)\,a(0) + P_t(1)\,a(0) + \ldots + P_t(n)\,a(0)$$

(If there are more than n customers in the system at the start then at least one of these will be in the system at the end).

$$P_{t+s}(1) = [P_t(0) + P_t(1) + \ldots + P_t(n)]\,a(1) + P_t(n+1)\,a(0)$$
$$P_{t+s}(j) = [P_t(0) + P_t(1) + \ldots + P_t(n)]\,a(j) + P_t(n+1)\,a(j-1)$$
$$+ \ldots + P_t(n+j)\,a(0) \qquad (3.14)$$
$$j = 1, 2, \ldots, \infty$$

The steady state probabilities are obtained by dropping the time dependence, giving

$$P(0) = [P(0) + P(1) + \ldots + P(n)]\,a(0)$$

$$P(j) = [P(0) + P(1) + \ldots + P(n)]\,a(j) + \sum_{k=1}^{k=j} P(n+k)\,a(j-k) \quad (3.15)$$

$$j = 1, 2, \ldots, \infty$$

The probabilities can be obtained directly from these equations by repeated substitution if the probabilities $P(0)$, $P(1)$, ..., $P(n-1)$ are known.

These can be found by considering the probability generating function

$$F(x) = \sum_{j=0}^{\infty} x^j P(j)$$

Multiplying the equations 3.15 by $x^0, x, x^2, \ldots, x^j, \ldots$ and summing all the resulting equations gives

$$F(x) = [P(0)+P(1)+P(2)+\ldots+P(n)] \sum_{j=0}^{\infty} x^j a(j)$$

$$+ \sum_{k=1}^{\infty} P(n+k)\, s(k)$$

where
$$s(k) = \sum_{j=0}^{\infty} x^{j+k}\, a(j)$$

$$= x^k\, e^{-\varrho(1-x)}$$

hence

$$F(x) = [P(0)+P(1)+\ldots+P(n)]e^{-\varrho(1-x)} + \sum_{k=1}^{\infty} x^k\, e^{-\varrho(1-x)}\, P(n+k)$$

$$= [P(0)+P(1)+\ldots+P(n)]e^{-\varrho(1-x)} + x^{-n}e^{-\varrho(1-x)} \sum_{k=1}^{\infty} x^{n+k} P(n+k)$$

$$= [P(0)+P(1)+\ldots P(n)]e^{-\varrho(1-x)}$$

$$+ x^{-n}e^{-\varrho(1-x)} \{F(x) - P(0) - xP(1) - \ldots - x^n P(n)\}$$

$$F(x)\,[1 - x^{-n}\, e^{-\varrho(1-x)}] = P(0)\,(1-x^{-n}) + P(1)\,(1-x^{-n+1})$$

$$+ P(2)\,(1-x^{-n+2}) + \ldots + P(n-1)$$

$$\times (1-x^{-1})\, [= \text{r.h.s, say}]$$

$$F(x) = (\text{r.h.s})/(1 - x^{-n}\, e^{-\varrho(1-x)})$$

$$= (\text{r.h.s})x^n/(x^n - e^{-\varrho(1-x)}) \qquad (3.16)$$

From its definition $F(x)$ is finite for any value of x which is less than 1 in absolute value. Any such value which is a root of the equation

$$x^n - e^{-\varrho(1-x)} = 0 \qquad (3.17)$$

will result in the denominator of the expression for $F(x)$ in equation 3.16 becoming zero. The right hand side would then be infinite unless the numerator is zero too. There are n such roots to this equation, which gives n equations for the probabilities $P(0)$, $P(1)$, $\ldots$, $P(n-1)$. If these roots are x_1, x_2, $\ldots$, x_n the equations are

$$P(0)(x_i^n - 1) + P(1)(x_i^n - x) + \ldots + P(n-1)(x_i^n - x^{n-1}) = 0$$
$$i = 1, 2, \ldots, n \qquad (3.18)$$

obviously $x = 1$ is a solution to equation 3.17 which is one of the roots, the corresponding equation 3.18 will reduce to the identity $0 = 0$. The equation for utilisation of the servers can be used in its place, namely

$$\text{Server utilisation} = \varrho/n = \frac{1}{n}\{0\,P(0) + 1\,P(1) + 2\,P(2) + \ldots$$

$$+ (n-1)\,P(n-1) + n[P(n) + P(n+1) + \ldots\,]\}$$
$$\varrho = n[1 - P(0) - P(1) - \ldots - P(n-1)] + P(1) + 2\,P(2) + \ldots +$$
$$+ (n-1)\,P(n-1)$$
$$n - \varrho = nP(0) + (n-1)\,P(1) + \ldots + 2\,P(n-2) + P(n-1) \qquad (3.19)$$

Having calculated the roots of equation 3.17 x_i, the probabilities $P(0)$, to $P(n-1)$ can be calculated from equations 3.19 and 3.18. These probabilities can be put in equations 3.15 to give in turn $P(n)$, $P(n+1)$, etc. Rounding errors will soon build up in the calculation of these probabilities, and an alternative approach may then have to be used. The approximate values of the probabilities found by direct substitution can be used as initial values for an iterative procedure in the equations 3.15. Using the values obtained in the expressions on the right hand side of equations 3.15 new estimates are obtained for $P(0)$, $P(1)$, $P(2)$, etc. If the difference between the new estimates of any probability and the initial estimate of the same probability is greater than any predetermined tolerance on the accuracy of the values, the new estimates are taken as initial values and the whole procedure repeated until the required accuracy is obtained.

Example 3.1

Calculate the steady state probabilities for a two server queue $M/D/2$, with arrival rate of one customer every two minutes and a service time of one minute.

$$\varrho = \frac{\text{arrival rate}}{\text{service rate}} = \frac{1}{2} = 0.5$$

The equation 3.17 gives

$$x^2 = e^{-(1-x)/2}$$

roots of this are $x = 1$ and $x = -0.660\,291$

equations for $P(0)$ and $P(1)$ are:

$$2 - \varrho = 2\,P(0) + P(1) = 1.5$$

$$P(0)\,(x^2 - 1) + P(1)\,(x^2 - x) = 0 \qquad x = -0.660\,291$$

i.e. $-0.564\,016\,P(0) + 1.096\,275\,P(1) = 0$

$$P(1) = 0.514\,484\,P(0)$$

$$2.514\,484\,P(0) = 1.5, \quad P(0) = 0.596\,544$$
$$P(1) = 0.306\,912$$

$$a(0) = e^{-\varrho} = 0.606\,531$$
$$a(1) = \varrho e^{-\varrho} = 0.303\,265$$
$$a(2) \qquad\quad = 0.075\,817$$
$$a(3) \qquad\quad = 0.012\,636$$
$$a(4) \qquad\quad = 0.001\,579$$
$$a(5) \qquad\quad = 0.000\,158$$
$$a(6) \qquad\quad = 0.000\,013$$
$$a(7) \qquad\quad = 0.000\,001$$

From equation 3.15

$$P(2) = \{P(0) - [P(0) + P(1)]\,a(0)\}/a(0) = 0.080\,078$$
$$P(3) = \{P(1) - [P(0) + P(1) + P(2)]\,a(1)\}/a(0) = 0.014\,245$$
$$P(4) = \{P(2) - [P(0) + P(1) + P(2)]\,a(2) - P(3)\,a(1)\}/a(0) = 0.001\,961$$
$$P(5) = \text{negative.}$$

Rounding errors have at this stage become sufficiently large to make the calculation of $P(5)$ impossible. As a first approximation take $P(j) = 0$ for $j \geqslant 5$ and the other values of the probabilities to be in the ratio of the values obtained with a sum of unity, this gives

$$P(0) = 0.596\,698$$
$$P(1) = 0.306\,992$$
$$P(2) = 0.080\,099$$
$$P(3) = 0.014\,249$$
$$P(4) = 0.001\,962$$

putting these values in the r.h.s. of equation 3.15 gives new values of:

$$P(0) = 0.596\,699$$
$$P(1) = 0.306\,991$$
$$P(2) = 0.080\,099$$
$$P(3) = 0.014\,106$$
$$P(4) = 0.001\,882$$
$$P(5) = 0.000\,203$$
$$P(6) = 0.000\,018$$
$$P(7) = 0.000\,001$$

The new values are not accurate enough if five figure accuracy is required for example and the process is now repeated until the required accuracy is obtained as shown in Table 3.1.

The estimates of the probabilities on the 6th and 7th cycle are the same to the accuracy of five decimal places and hence are the required steady state solutions to the probability equations. It can be seen that the probabilities $P(0)$ and $P(1)$ have stabilised at figures which are in agreement with the values found initially from the generating function equations, namely $P(0) = 0.596\,544$ and $P(1) = 0.306\,912$.

Factors of interest can be calculated either from the probabilities $P(j)$ or from the probability generating function $F(x)$.

Average number of customers in the system

$$= \sum_{j=0}^{\infty} jP(j) = \frac{\mathrm{d}}{\mathrm{d}x} F(x) \bigg|_{x=1}$$

The use of the generating function involves the calculation of only the first n probabilities $P(0)$ to $P(n-1)$ as can be seen from equation 3.16. This avoids the iterative procedure required for the calculation of the probabilities $P(j)$ with higher values of j and is hence likely to be shorter. From equation 3.16

$$F(x) = G(x)/[x^n - \mathrm{e}^{-\varrho(1-x)}]$$

where

$$G(x) = \sum_{j=0}^{n-1} P(j)(x^n - x^j)$$

$$\frac{\mathrm{d}F(x)}{\mathrm{d}x} = \left\{ \sum_{j=1}^{n-1} P(j)(nx^{n-1} - jx^{j-1}) + nx^{n-1} P(0) \right\} \Big/ [x^n - \mathrm{e}^{-\varrho(1-x)}]$$
$$- G(x)(nx^{n-1} - \varrho \mathrm{e}^{-\varrho(1-x)})/[x^n - \mathrm{e}^{-\varrho(1-x)}]^2$$

Table 3.1. VALUES OF $P(n)$

n	2nd cycle	3rd cycle	4th cycle	5th cycle	6th cycle	7th cycle
0	0·596 699	0·596 699	0·596 593	0·596 560	0·596 549	0·596 546
1	0·306 991	0·306 904	0·306 905	0·306 909	0·306 911	0·306 911
2	0·080 099	0·080 007	0·080 059	0·080 075	0·080 079	0·080 080
3	0·014 106	0·014 195	0·014 230	0·014 239	0·014 241	0·014 242
4	0·001 882	0·001 945	0·001 961	0·001 964	0·001 965	0·001 965
5	0·000 203	0·000 223	0·000 227	0·000 228	0·000 228	0·000 228
6	0·000 018	0·000 022	0·000 023	0·000 023	0·000 023	0·000 023
7	0·000 001	0·000 002	0·000 002	0·000 002	0·000 002	0·000 002

when $x = 1$ both the numerator and denominator are zero and so the ratio of the differentials of each of these must be used to obtain the value. When these have been calculated and evaluated at $x = 1$ the expression obtained is:

$$\left. \frac{\mathrm{d}F(x)}{\mathrm{d}x} \right|_{x=1} = A/(n-\varrho) \qquad (3.20)$$

where $2A = n(n-1)\,(P(0)+P(1)) + \sum\limits_{j=2}^{n-1} P(j)\,[n(n-1)-j(j-1)]$

$$-(n-\varrho)^2 + n \qquad (3.21)$$

Hence,

Average number of customers in system $= A/(n-\varrho)$

Average number of customers in the queue

$$= \sum_{i=n}^{\infty} (i-n)\,P(i) = \sum_{i=0}^{\infty} iP(i) - n + \sum_{i=0}^{n-1} (n-i)\,P(i)$$

$$= A/(n-\varrho) - n + n - \varrho \quad \text{from equations 3.21 and 3.19}$$

$$= A/(n-\varrho) - \varrho \qquad (3.22)$$

The distribution of waiting time has been obtained by Prabhu[8] and will not be derived here. The average waiting time can be found by more direct consideration of the queue size when a customer arrives at the system for service. If a customer arrives to find less than n servers in the system he will not have to wait, hence

chance a customer does not have to wait $= \sum\limits_{j=0}^{n-1} P(j)$ $\qquad$ (3.23)

The average waiting time in the steady state can be shown to be related to the average number of customers in the queue and the arrival rate of customers by the formula

$$L = \lambda W$$

where $\quad L =$ the average number of customers in the queue

$\quad\ \ \lambda =$ the arrival rate of customers

$\quad\ \ W =$ the average waiting time of customers.

Proofs of the formula have been given by Little,[10] Jewell,[11] and Eilon.[12] If after a time T

$A(T)$ = The total waiting time of all customers in, or having been in, the system up to time T

$N(T)$ = The total number of arrivals to the system up to time T

L = the limit of $A(T)/T$ as $T \to \infty$

W = the limit of $A(T)/N(T)$ as $T \to \infty$

λ = the limit of $N(T)/T$ as $T \to \infty$

since
$$\frac{A(T)}{N(T)} \frac{N(T)}{T} = \frac{A(T)}{T}$$

Provided the three limits exist, which is true of systems which are not overloaded and the steady state conditions of such systems, then

$$W\lambda = L$$

The result means that only one of the factors L or W need be calculated for the other to be obtained from the formula. The value most easily found from the steady state probabilities is L and hence the formula is usually used to determine W. If the distribution of waiting time is required then a more detailed study is required as mentioned above.

The average busy period of the system $= [1 - P(0)]/[\lambda P(0)]$

The average busy period of individual servers $= \bar{B} = \varrho \bar{I}/(n - \varrho)$ using exactly the same arguments as for equation 2.53.

Where $\bar{I}$, the average idle period of a server, with the service discipline of first idle first back for service is

$$\bar{I} = \sum_{j=0}^{n-1} a(j)(n-j)/\lambda$$

where $a(j) = P(j) \Big/ \sum_{j=0}^{n-1} P(j)$

$$\bar{I} = \sum_{j=0}^{n-1} P(j)(n-j) \Big/ \left(\lambda \sum_{0}^{n-1} P(j) \right) = (n-\varrho) \Big/ \left(\lambda \sum_{0}^{n-1} P(j) \right)$$

hence
$$\bar{B} = \varrho/\lambda \sum_{0}^{n-1} P(j) = s \Big/ \sum_{0}^{n-1} P(j) \qquad (3.24)$$

Tables of results for this queue are given in the table section. Table A.2 gives the average waiting time for 2 to 10 servers with utilisation from 0·1 to 0·9 in steps of 0·1. Table A.7 gives the chance a customer does not have to wait over the same range of servers and utilisation. The average busy period of individual servers is not tabulated since it can be obtained so easily from the chance a customer does not have to wait using equation 3.24.

Other numerical data is already published on this queue, Shelton[9] gives graphs of the average waiting time values of n from 1 to 100 and values of utilisation 0·1, (0·1), 0·7, (0·05), 0·95, and 0·96.

Example 3.2

An unloading jetty for ships importing iron ore is being developed at a steel works. It costs £40 000 per annum to run a berth capable of unloading a ship in 12 h, this time being constant for all ships. The ships arrive at random at a rate of 3 a day. The steel company pays the ship owners demurrage of £1 000 for every day a ship is delayed waiting to unload at the jetty. What is the optimum number of berths for the steel company to run at the jetty?

Since the unloading times are constant and the arrival of ships random the system is of the form $M/D/n$, where n is the number of berths.

The utilisation of the system is $\lambda/n\mu = 3/2n$
The annual running cost = £40 000 n
The annual demurrage = $3 \times 365 \times £1\,000 \times$ average waiting time
for $n = 2$, $u = 0·75$, average waiting time = $0·667\,3 \times \frac{1}{2}$ days.
    Annual cost = £80 000 + 0·333 82 × 3 × 365 × 1 000 = £425 548
for $n = 3$, $u = 0·5$, average waiting time = $0·087\,2 \times \frac{1}{2}$ days.
    Annual Cost = £120 000 + 47 742 = £167 742
for $n = 4$, $u = 0·375$, average waiting time = $0·017\,8 \times \frac{1}{2}$ days.
    Annual cost = £160 000 + 9 746 = £169 746

The figures for waiting time are found by linear interpolation on the logarithm of waiting time at adjacent values of utilisation in Table A.2 when the required utilisation is not tabulated.

The optimum number of berths to run can be seen to be three.

Example 3.3

A factory manufacturing cattle foods supplies the bulk of its product to dealers who collect their requirements from the factory in lorries. The arrival of lorries is random at the rate of twenty four per hour. It is planned to provide eight loading bays each capable of taking one lorry for this supply. The loading time of lorries is always ten minutes. What will be the average waiting time of lorries in the steady state and what proportion of lorries will not have to queue for service?

The arrival rate of lorries $= 24/h$
The service rate of servers $= 6/h$
The number of servers $= 8$
The utilisation of the system $= \lambda/n\mu = 24/8 \times 6 = 0.5$

hence average waiting time of lorries (from Table A.2) $= 0.0093 \times 10$ min

$$= 0.09 \text{ min}$$

The chance a lorry does not have to wait for service (from Table A.7)

$$= 0.9457$$

so only 5.43% of lorries have to wait with the specified loading facilities.

3.4 PROBLEMS

1. A factory general stores has three servers continuously available at which customers arrive in a Poisson stream whose service time is constant. The service time is such that the utilisation of the system is 80% and the steady state probabilities of the system being empty of customers or only having one customer are $P(0) = 0.04984$ and $P(1) = 0.13286$ respectively. The stores is reorganised and the service time is halved and is still invariable; the new values of the steady state probabilities are: $P(0) = 0.28898$ and $P(1) = 0.35585$

By what proportion does the average waiting time decrease with the change in service time? Check the result by referring to Table A.2.

2. A port to unload container vessels is being developed. The number

of berths in the port is planned to be 7, continuously available. The arrival of ships is expected to be random with an average of six per day. The time each ship will occupy a berth is expected to be constant since the ships are all of the same type. What berth time should be planned if 70% of ships do not have to wait for unloading because all berths are occupied?

3. The manager of a car showroom wants to decide on the number of assistants he needs in the showroom to serve customers. The time taken to attend to a customer is constant at 10 min, and customers arrive at random at a rate of 20 an hour. The manager must ensure that the average busy period of an assistant is not longer than 20 min, and he also wishes to ensure the average waiting time of customers is less than one minute. How many assistants will he need if steady state conditions apply?

4. A steelworks has three berths at its iron ore unloading terminal. Each berth is capable of unloading a ship in 12 h; there being no variation in the unloading time. Ships arrive at random at the rate of three a day. The size of the harbour holding the jetty must be sufficiently large so that 99% of the time there is room for the ships being unloaded and queueing. How many ships must the harbour be capable of holding?

CHAPTER 4

The Queue $D/M/n$

This queue is the third case possible with the two distributions, negative exponential and constant appearing in the arrival pattern or service times. It is the last of interest because the final combination $D/D/n$ is a trivial case where no queueing occurs at all unless the service system is overloaded in which case of course queues will build up as the system continues running. The four cases $M/M/n$, $M/D/n$, $D/M/n$, $D/D/n$, can be thought of as extreme cases for most practical situations and can give bounds to any practical problem. The system itself $(D/M/n)$ occurs in practice in appointment systems.

4.1 MATHEMATICAL DEVELOPMENT OF $D/M/n$

Since the arrivals are now at constant intervals the approach for developing the probability equations can be taken from that used for constant service times, which is to consider the system at intervals of a service time. In this case however the interval will be the length of the constant arrival interval. Also let the start of the interval be a point at which a customer arrives.

Let

$P_t(j)$ = the chance there are j customrs in the system at time t, a point at which a customer arrives. Where j includes the customer just arrived. Only departures from the system will occur in the interval from t to $t+a$ when the next customer arrives.

Let $d_j(i)$ = the chance i customers will depart in the interval when there are j customers in the system at the start.

The equations for the probabilities $P_t(j)$ are:

$$P_{t+a}(1) = \sum_{j=1}^{\infty} P_t(j)\, d_j(j)$$

$$P_{t+a}(2) = \sum_{j=1}^{\infty} P_t(j)\, d_j(j-1)$$

$$P_{t+a}(k) = \sum_{j=k-1}^{\infty} P_t(j)\, d_j(j-k+1) \qquad (4.1)$$

$$k = 2, 3, \ldots, \infty$$

The departure probabilities $d_j(i)$ take two distinct forms, one for $j \leqslant n$ and one for $j > n$. Consider first the case where $j \leqslant n$. In this situation all customers will be being served at the start of the interval, so when a server finishes service he will not commence service on any other customer. The chance any one server will complete service in the interval of length a is the chance the remainder of the service left at the start of the interval is less than a. Since the service time has a negative exponential distribution, the remainder will have the same distribution as the full service time, which gives the chance of a server completing service as

$$p = \int_0^a \mu\, e^{-\mu t}\, dt = 1 - e^{-a\mu} = 1 - e^{-a/s} \qquad (4.2)$$

a = average interval arrival;
s = average service time.

The distribution of the number of customers completing service is now a binomial distribution, since the servers operate independently, giving

$$d_j(i) = \binom{j}{i} p^i q^{j-i} \qquad (4.3)$$

When $j > n$ there are some customers queueing for service so servers on completing service have to commence service on further customers until this queue is eliminated at which point the consideration is similar to that above for the remainder of the interval.

$$d_j(i) = \left(\frac{na}{s}\right)^i \frac{e^{(-na)/s}}{i!} , \qquad i \leqslant j-n-1 \tag{4.4}$$

$$d_j(i) = \int_{t=0}^{a} \frac{n}{s}\left(\frac{nt}{s}\right)^{j-n-1} \frac{e^{(-nt)/s}}{(j-n-1)!} \binom{n}{i-j+n} p(a-t)^{i-j+n}$$

$$q(a-t)^{j-i} \, dt$$

$$i \geqslant j-n \tag{4.5}$$

where
$$p(t) = 1 - e^{-t/s} = 1 - q(t)$$

This particular model was studied by D. G. Kendall[1] who showed the values of $P(j)$ follow a geometric progression for $j > n-1$ in the steady state.

The solution is hence

$$\left.\begin{array}{ll} P(j) = \mu_j/K & j \leqslant n-1 \\ P(j) = \lambda^{j-n}/K & j > n-1 \end{array}\right\} \tag{4.6}$$

$$K = \sum_{j=1}^{n-1} \mu_j + 1/(1-\lambda)$$

the value of λ is given by:

$$e^{-(1-\lambda)na/s} = \lambda$$

i.e.
$$1 - e^{-x} = \varrho x \tag{4.7}$$

where
$$x = (1-\lambda)/\varrho$$

Since the value of λ dependes only on ϱ it is a simple matter to calculate the values of λ which are applicable to any number of servers, n (see Table 4.1).

Table 4.1.

ϱ	λ	ϱ	λ
0·0	0	0·6	0·324 2
0·1	$0·454\,2\times10^{-4}$	0·7	0·467 0
0·2	$0·697\,7\times10^{-2}$	0·8	0·628 6
0·3	$0·408\,8\times10^{-1}$	0·9	0·806 9
0·4	0·107 36	1·0	1·0
0·5	0·203 2		

The only values of $P(j)$ still undetermined are the values for $j \ll n-1$. These can be found from the equation 4.1 for $k = 2, 3, \ldots, n$. If these equations are taken in reverse order $k = n, (n-1), \ldots, 3, 2$, it is found that $\mu_{n-1}, \mu_{n-2}, \ldots, \mu$, can be evaluated in turn in terms of functions of the probabilities $d_j(i)$.

$$1 = \mu_{n-1}\, d_{n-1}(0) + d_n(1) + \sum_{j=1}^{\infty} \lambda^i\, d_{n+i}(i+1)$$

$$\mu_j = \mu_{j-1}\, d_{j-1}(0) + \mu_j\, d_j(1) + \ldots + \mu_{n-1}\, d_{n-1}(n-j)$$
$$+ \sum_{i=1}^{\infty} \lambda^i\, d_{n+i}(n+1-j+1)$$
$$j = n-1, n-2, \ldots, 2$$

$$\mu_2 = \mu_1\, d_1(0) + \ldots + \mu_{n-1}\, d_{n-1}(n-2) + \sum_{i=1}^{\infty} \lambda^i\, d_{n+i}(n+i-1) \quad (4.8)$$

The coefficients in these equations are simple to evaluate except the summation term at the right of each equation. If

$$g_j(\lambda) = \sum_{i=1}^{\infty} \lambda^i\, d_{n+i}(n+1-j+1)$$

by substitution and summation this reduces to

$$g_j(\lambda) = \int_0^a \frac{n}{s}\, e^{\frac{-nt}{s}(1-\lambda)} \binom{n}{n-j+1} p(a-t)^{n-j+1}\, q(a-t)^{i-1}\, \mathrm{d}t$$

$$= n\, e^{\frac{-na}{s}(1-\lambda)} \binom{n}{n-j+1} \int_{e^{\frac{-a}{s}}}^{1} (1-v)^{n-j+1}\, v^{j-2-n(1-\lambda)}\, \mathrm{d}v$$

$$= n\lambda \binom{n}{n-j+1} \int_{e^{\frac{-a}{s}}}^{1} (1-v)^{n-j+1}\, v^{j-2-n(1-\lambda)}\, \mathrm{d}v \quad (4.9)$$

$$j = 2, 3, \ldots, n-1$$

While this is cumbersome for algebraic reduction its evaluation numerically once j, and λ are known is straightforward. This enables the values μ_1 to μ_{n-1} to be evaluated and hence the probabilities $P(j)$. The factors of interest with respect to customers can now be calculated.

Chance a customer does not have to wait

$$= \sum_{j=1}^{n} P(j) = c = (1+\Sigma\mu_j)/K. \tag{4.10}$$

Chance there are no customers waiting for service immediately before a customer arrives

$$= \sum_{j=1}^{n+1} P(j)$$

$$= (\lambda+1+\Sigma\mu_j)/K \tag{4.11}$$

The distribution of waiting time as shown by Kendall[1], if a customer has to wait is $f(t)$, where

$$f(t) = re^{-rt} : r = \frac{n}{s}(1-\lambda)$$

The average waiting time over all customers

$$= \frac{s}{n} \cdot \frac{(1-c)}{(1-\lambda)} \tag{4.12}$$

The steady state probabilities calculated here apply only at points in time when customers arrive and cannot be used for calculating busy periods of the system as a whole or of individual servers.

The numerical results for this model are then only the average waiting time (Table A.3) and the chance of not having to wait (Table A.8).

Example 4.1

A hospital outpatient department runs an appointment system for non emergency cases. The consulting times for individual patients has a negative exponential distribution with an average of 4 min. The number of patients in the system is thirty an hour. If the average waiting time of patients is to be kept down to two minutes how many doctors will be required for the system? What will their utilisation be?

The waiting time of patients can be found from Table A.3 once the number of doctors is known. The arrival rate is 30 per hour, and the service rate 15 per hour. At least three doctors will be needed for steady state conditions to apply.

For three and more doctors in the system the waiting times are:[1]

$n = 3$, $u = \frac{2}{3}$ $W = 0 \cdot 1254 \times 4$ min (interpolating on the logarithm of W)

$$= 0 \cdot 5016 \text{ min.}$$

Three doctors will be sufficient to keep the waiting time below two minutes on average.

The utilisation of the doctors will be 67%.

Example 4.2

It is forecast that planes will be scheduled to arrive at an airport at a steady rate of one every three minutes and the time a plane occupies a terminal is expected to have a negative exponential distribution with an average of 20 min. If the cost of delaying a plane is £1 000 per hour and the cost of running a terminal is £500 per hour, how many terminals should there be at the airport? Using the table of average waiting time the delays and costs are calculated to be as shown in Table 4.2.

Table 4.2.

Number of Terminals	Average Delay to Planes (minutes)	Terminal per hour (£)	Delay Cost per hour (£)	Total Hourly Cost (£)
8	2·871 4	4 000	957·13	4 957
9	0·638 0	4 500	212·67	4 713
10	0·152 0	5 000	50·67	5 051

So nine terminals are required at the airport.

4.2 PROBLEMS

1. A plant has a batch of semi-finished material delivered each morning from the main factory. Each batch is delivered in a container which remains with it until processing is complete, when the container is then used to return the batch to the factory. The plant has two lines capable of processing the semi-finished material, each line can deal with only one batch at a time. The processing time per batch has a negative exponential distribution with an average of 1·3 days. What is the minimum number of containers required to ensure that on only one day in every thousand there will be no delay because there is no container available for delivery of that day's batch? It may be assumed that return and delivery of containers takes a negligible length of time.

2. A group medical practice operates a system of having two doctors at each surgery, patients being seen in order of arrival by whichever doctor becomes first available. Arrivals of patients and consulting times both have negative exponential distributions, the arrival rate being one patient every 3 min and the consulting time being 5 min on average.

It is found that the majority of patients at surgery are nonurgent cases and in an effort to reduce the waiting time at the surgery patients phone and make appointments for consultations. The arrival rate of patients is now constant at one every 3 min. By what amount is the average waiting time decreased by the introduction of the appointment system?

3. A works general stores has six servers at the issue counter of the stores to deal with demand from the works. The arrival intervals and service times are negative exponential with averages of 2 min and 8 min respectively. Because of the high variability in arrival of customers an appointment system is instituted with customers arriving regularly every two minutes. If the average waiting time is to be kept not less than the waiting time in the old system what is the smallest number of servers which can be released from the counter for other duties in the stores?

CHAPTER 5

Queues with More General Distributions of Arrival and Service Time

5.1 INTRODUCTION

The queues studied so far have been restricted in the form of distribution the arrival intervals and service time take, the two forms being constant and negative exponential. These can in practice be considered as distributions which are at the extremes of likely variability, the constant distribution having no variability and the negative exponential having a very high variability. The coefficient variation of the negative exponential distribution is unity, i.e. its standard deviation is equal to its mean.

Queues having these two distributions have been studied first because the mathematics involved is more tractable and the results for these special cases are of use in putting limits on the values of average queue size etc., for more practical queue models.

In making the models more general a distribution must be used which is more flexible than the constant or negative exponential distributions in that at least the mean and standard deviation can be made equal to that of the practical problem and yet maintain some of the properties of the negative exponential distribution which made its mathematical development tractable. A. K. Erlang of the Copenhagen Telephone Company first studied such a distribution. He considered the distribution of a time which is divided into a fixed number of 'phases' each phase having a negative exponential distribution. If there are k 'phases' and the average length of each phase is $1/\lambda$ units, then it has already been shown (equation 2.28) that the distribution function $f(t)$ is:

$$f(t) = \lambda^k t^{k-1} \frac{e^{-\lambda t}}{(k-1)!} \tag{5.1}$$

The mean of this distribution is

$$E(t) = k/\lambda \tag{5.2}$$

and its standard deviation

$$(E(t^2) - E(t)^2)^{1/2} = k^{1/2}/\lambda \tag{5.3}$$

The appropriate values of k and λ for the representation of a distribution taken from a practical situation by the Erlang distribution (equation 5.1) can be found by equating moments. If m is the mean of the actual distribution and s its standard deviation then $k/\lambda = m$ and

$$s = k^{1/2}/\lambda$$

by division,

$$k = m^2/s^2$$

or $k^{-1} =$ (coefficient of variation)^2 $\tag{5.4}$

and $\lambda^{-1} = m/k$ $\tag{5.5}$

The value of k must be an integer for the Erlang distribution and there is no guarantee that the value given by equation 5.4 will be an integer, in such cases the integers nearest above and below the value given by the equation should be used, to give bounds on the actual distribution. As mentioned in the introduction the notation used by Kendall for this form of distribution is E_k where k is the number of 'phases'.

5.2 MATHEMATICAL APPROACH TO $E_k/E_l/1$

Let a be the average arrival interval between customers, then if the distribution of arrival intervals is of the form E_k its distribution function is

$$g(t) = \left(\frac{k}{a}\right)^k t^{k-1} \frac{e^{-kt/a}}{(k-1)!} \tag{5.6}$$

Similarly for a service time distribution with average s and form E_l the distribution function is

$$f(t) = \left(\frac{l}{s}\right)^l t^{l-1} \frac{e^{-lt/s}}{(l-1)!} \tag{5.7}$$

Let $P(m, n; j) = $ the steady state probability there are j customers in the system, the one being served having m of the l 'phases' of service still to complete, the next arrival having n of the k 'phases' still to complete.

$$\left.\begin{array}{l} j = 1, 2, \ldots, \infty \\ m = 1, 2, \ldots, l \\ n = 1, 2, \ldots, k \end{array}\right\} \tag{5.8}$$

$P(n; 0) = $ the steady state probability the system is empty and the next arrival has n of the k 'phases' still to complete.

$$n = 1, 2, \ldots, k$$

If $\lambda = k/a$ and $\mu = l/s$ the equations for the probabilities are, (using the same approach as for the equations for $M/M/n$):

$$(\lambda+\mu)\, P(m, n; j) = \mu P(m+1, n; j) + \lambda P(m, n+1; j)$$
$$j = 1, 2, \ldots, \infty$$
$$m = 1, 2, \ldots, l-1$$
$$n = 1, 2, \ldots, k-1$$

$$(\lambda+\mu)\, P(l, n; j) = \mu P(1, n; j-1) + \lambda P(l, n+1; j)$$
$$j = 2, 3, \ldots, \infty$$
$$n = 1, 2, \ldots, k-1$$

$$(\lambda+\mu)\, P(m, k; j) = \mu P(m+1, k; j) + \lambda P(m, 1; j-1)$$
$$j = 1, 2, \ldots, \infty$$
$$m = 1, 2, \ldots, l-1$$

$$(\lambda+\mu)\, P(l, k; j) = \mu P(1, k; j-1) + \lambda P(l, 1; j-1)$$
$$j = 2, 3, \ldots, \infty$$

$$(\lambda+\mu)\, P(l, n; 1) = \lambda P(l, n+1; 1)$$
$$n = 1, 2, \ldots, k-1$$

$$(\lambda+\mu)\, P(l, k; 1) = \lambda P(1; 0) + \mu P(l, 1; 2)$$
$$\lambda P(n; 0) = \lambda P(n+1; 0) + \mu P(1, n; 1)$$
$$n = 1, 2, \ldots, k-1$$
$$\lambda P(k; 0) = \mu P(1, k; 1)$$

Prabhu[8] (p. 162) obtains formulae for the queue length distribution for the queue $G/E_s/1$ of which this is a special case, and the reader is referred to Prabhu for further development of these probabilities.

5.2.1 Distribution of Waiting Time

While the probability equations are not algebraically soluble, it is possible to obtain the distribution of waiting time by other methods. The derivation is given in Prabhu[8] (p. 170) and only the results are quoted here.

Let

$F(t)$ be the cumulative of the distribution function of waiting time t.
Then

$$F(t) = 1 - \sum_{r=1}^{l} A_r e^{-\theta_r t} \tag{5.9}$$

where

$$A_r = (1 - \theta_r s/l)^l \prod_{p \neq r}^{l} \left(\frac{1}{1 - \theta_r/\theta_p} \right) \tag{5.10}$$

$$r = 1, 2, \ldots, l$$

where θ_r are the roots with positive real part of

$$(l/s - \theta)^l = \left(\frac{l}{s} \right)^l \psi(\theta) \tag{5.11}$$

$\psi(\theta)$ being the Laplace transform of the inter arrival distribution (equation 5.6), i.e.

$$\psi(\theta) = \int_{e}^{\infty} e^{-\theta t} g(t) \, dt$$

$$= \left(\frac{k/a}{k/a + \theta} \right)^k \tag{5.12}$$

the equation 5.11 becomes

$$(l/s - \theta)^l (k/a + \theta)^k = \left(\frac{l}{s} \right)^l \left(\frac{k}{a} \right)^k. \tag{5.13}$$

The chance of not having to wait is $F(0)$

$$= 1 - \sum_{r=1}^{l} A_r \tag{5.14}$$

and the average waiting time $= \int_0^\infty x \, dF(x)$

$$= \sum_{r=1}^{l} A_r/\theta_r \tag{5.15}$$

The value of average waiting time, in units of average service time has been calculated from these formulae for a range of values of u, the utilisation of the system, l, and k. There is no restriction on k taking integer values, since the distribution function (equation 5.1) then becomes the generalisation of the Erlang distribution, the Pearson Type III distribution (see Elderton[13]). The square of the coefficient of variation of the distribution is $1/k$, values of k are taken such that their reciprocals are 0·1, 0·2, ..., 0·9, 1·0. Utilisations are taken from 0·1 to 0·9 in steps of 0·1, and l is taken in steps of one from 1 to 10. The results are given in table A.5.

5.3 USE OF THE TABLES OF WAITING TIME

The tables can be interpolated to obtain values of average waiting time for intermediate values of utilisation u and coefficients of variation of arrival and service time distributions. Linear interpolation with respect to the utilisation u is most accurate on the logarithm of waiting time.

Let $v_a =$ (coefficient of variation of arrival intervals)^2

$\quad =$ variance of arrival interval/(average arrival interval)^2 (5.16)

and $v_s =$ (coefficient of variation of service time)^2

$\quad =$ variance of service time/(average service time)^2 (5.17)

v_a and v_s are measures of the degree of variability in the distributions of arrival interval and service time respectively. The effect of changes in variability in the distributions on waiting time can be shown graphically for particular levels of utilisation. Figure 5.1 shows the graph for a high utilisation $u = 0.9$ and Figure 5.2 shows the graph for a low utilisation $u = 0.1$.

For high utilisations as Figure 5.1 clearly shows there is a linear relationship between waiting time and v_s for any given value of v_a as can be seen from the line *AB* drawn for $v_a = 0.5$ and similar lines for $v_a = 0.1$ and 0.2. Conversely, there is also a linear relationship between waiting time and v_s for fixed values of v_a as the line *CD* shows for $v_a = 0.5$.

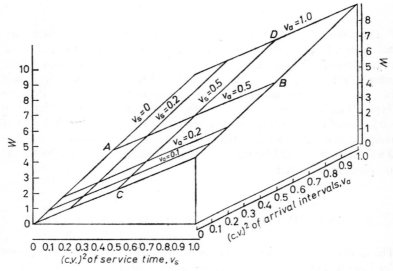

Fig. 5.1

Values of waiting time can be found for any values of v_a and v_s by linear interpolation between the tabulated values for high utilisations.

For low utilisations as Figure 5.2 shows for $u = 0.1$ linear interpolation would not give such good results. The interpolation is reasonably good for values of v_s for fixed values of v_a since the curve *AB* and similar ones are only slightly curved.

The graphs for fixed values of v_s such as *CD* are more curved making linear interpolation less accurate. However the values tabulated are sufficiently frequent along these curves to give reasonable accuracy in the estimates of waiting time.

In practice the low values of utilisation are less important because they occur infrequently, the values of waiting time are very low at low utilisations. Figure 5.2 has a vertical scale of W which is 100 times that of Figure 5.1 since plotting in on the same scale would have resulted in a surface which was almost entirely in the base plane of Figure 5.1.

Linear interpolation on v_a and v_s should in most practical cases give sufficiently accurate results, the accuracy being to the second decimal place in W in most cases.

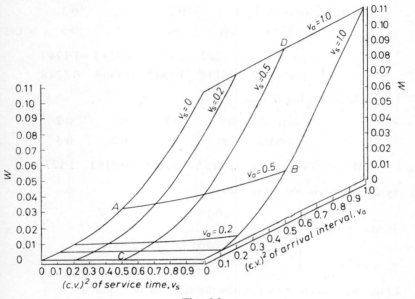

Fig. 5.2

Example 5.1

The distribution of inter arrival times at a general stores has an average of 6·7 min and a standard deviation of 2·2 min. The service times of the customers has an average of 5·3 min with a standard deviation of 4·3 min. The distributions can be assumed to have the Erlang form; how much will the average waiting time be at the stores with a single server?

The utilisation of the system is $5·3/6·7 = 0·791$

The coefficient of variation of arrival time = s.d./mean

$$= 2 \cdot 2/6 \cdot 7 = 0 \cdot 328$$

so $v_a = $ (c.v.)^2 of arrival time = $(0 \cdot 328)^2$ = $0 \cdot 108$

The coefficient of variation of service time = $4 \cdot 3/5 \cdot 3 = 0 \cdot 811$

and (c.v.)^2 of service time = $(0 \cdot 811)^2 = 0 \cdot 658 = v_s$

From the tables of waiting time (Table A.5)

$v_a = $ (c.v.)^2 of arrival	0·1	0·2	0·1	0·2	
$v_s = $ (c.v.)^2 of service	1·0	1·0	0·5	0·5	$(= 1/l)$

$$W \begin{cases} u = 0 \cdot 8 & 1 \cdot 9222 & 2 \cdot 1523 & 0 \cdot 9744 & 1 \cdot 1947 \\ u = 0 \cdot 7 & 1 \cdot 0198 & 1 \cdot 1642 & 0 \cdot 4908 & 0 \cdot 6248 \end{cases}$$

Interpolating on log W gives

$v_a = $ (c.v.)^2 arrival	0·1	0·2	0·1	0·2
$v_s = $ (c.v.)^2 service	1·0	1·0	0·5	0·5
$W(u = 0 \cdot 791)$	1·8155	2·0366	0·9161	1·1272

Linear interpolation on v_s gives

	v_a	0·1	0·2
W at $u = 0 \cdot 791$ and $v_s = 0 \cdot 658$		1·2003	1·4177

Linear interpolation on v_a gives the value of W required,

for $u = 0 \cdot 791$

$v_s = $ (c.v.)^2 of service = $0 \cdot 658$

and $v_a = $ (c.v.)^2 of arrival = $0 \cdot 108$, to be $1 \cdot 2177$

Example 5.2

What is the maximum variability of the service time in a single server queue if the average waiting time of customers is to be less than 1·5 times the average service time? The average arrival interval between customers is 5·7 min and the (c.v.)² of arrival distribution is 0·63. The average service time is 4·5 min. Both distributions have the Erlang form.

The utilisation of the system $= 4·5/5·7 = 0·789$

$$v_a = \text{(c.v.)}^2 \text{ of arrival distribution} = 0·63$$

from the tables, interpolating for utilisation $= 0·789$ gives

     $v_s =$ (c.v.)² of service time $(= 1/l)$ 0·200   0·25
           average waiting time   1·475 7   1·567 4

interpolation gives waiting time equal to $1·5\times$(service time) when

$$v_s = \text{(c.v.)}^2 \text{ of service time} = 0·213\,2$$

So the highest value the standard deviation of service time can take if the average waiting time is not to exceed $1·5\times$(service time) is $4·5\times(0·2132)^{1/2}$

$$= 2·08 \text{ min}$$

5.3.1 A simple approximation to Average Waiting Time for $E_k/E_l/1$ from extreme cases

The Erlang distribution (equation 5.1) has the negative exponential form when $k = 1$ and the deterministic form when $k = \infty$. The queues $M/M/1$, $D/M/1$, $M/D/1$, and $D/D/1$ can then be thought of as extreme cases of this queue. It has been shown from Figure 5.1 that linear interpolation on v_a and v_s gives reasonable approximations to waiting times at intermediate values not given in Table A.5. The extreme cases should hence be able to give reasonable approximations to all values on the surface because of the linearity of the sections.

For $M/M/1$ $v_a = 1,$ $v_s = 1$
        $D/M/1$ $v_a = 0,$ $v_s^1 = 1$
        $M/D/1$ $v_a = 1,$ $v_s = 0$
        $D/D/1$ $v_a = 0,$ $v_s = 0$

The queue $D/D/1$ as mentioned previously has no variability in arrival intervals or service time and hence no queues develop in this situation so average waiting time is zero in all cases where the utilisation is less than or equal to unity.

If $W(v_a, v_s, u)$ is the average waiting time in units of service time in the queue $E_k/E_l/1$ with utilisation u then

$$v_a = k^{-1} \quad \text{and} \quad v_s = l^{-1}$$

$W(1, 1, u)$ is the average waiting time in the queue $M/M/1$

$W(0, 1, u)$ is the average waiting time in the queue $D/M/1$

$W(1, 0, u)$ is the average waiting time in the queue $M/D/1$

$W(0, 0, u)$ is the average waiting time in the queue $D/D/1$

because of the linearity of the surface on the v_a, v_s scales an approximation to $W(v_a, v_s, u)$ is

$$W(v_a, v_s, u) = (1-v_a)(1-v_s)\,W(0, 0, u) + (1-v_a)\,v_s W(0, 1, u)$$
$$+ v_a(1-v_s)\,W(1, 0, u) + v_a v_s W(1, 1, u)$$

since $W(0, 0, u) = 0$ this reduces to

$$W(v_a, v_s, u) = (1-v_a)\,v_s W(0, 1, u) + v_a(1-v_s)\,W(1, 0, u)$$
$$+ v_a v_s W(1, 1, u) \tag{5.18}$$

This relationship will give exact agreement at any point where v_a or v_s is either 0 or 1 so values at an intermediate point must be taken to test the accuracy of the approximation. If the central point $v_a = v_s = 0.5$ is taken, corresponding to $k = 2$, $l = 2$ and the model $E_2/E_2/1$ the comparisons are as shown in Table 5.1.

Table 5.1.

utilisation	Approximation $W(\tfrac{1}{2}, \tfrac{1}{2}, u)$ from equations 5.18	W for $E_2\mid E_2\mid 1$	Error in Approximation (%)
0·9	4·419 7	4·359 0	+ 1·4
0·8	1·923 1	1·865 3	+ 3·1
0·7	1·094 1	1·039 1	+ 5·3
0·6	0·682 4	0·630 6	+ 8·2
0·5	0·449 8	0·390 4	+ 15·2
0·4	0·280 1	0·235 5	+ 18·9
0·3	0·171 4	0·131 0	+ 30·8
0·2	0·095 5	0·060 4	+ 58·1
0·1	0·041 7	0·016 6	+151·2

The coefficients of variation were taken as 0·5 in each case as these are the points one could expect the linear approximation to be least accurate. It shows the linear interpolation always overestimates the average waiting time and that the percentage error is least at the high utilisations which are the ones usually of interest.

5.3.2 Distribution of Waiting Time in the General Single Server Queue

The previous chapters deal with queues with special forms of arrival pattern and service time distributions. The usefulness of the results is limited to the occasions when such special distributions are applicable to the practical queueing situation. The results quoted here are for more general forms of distribution. The first is a result derived by Prabhu[8] (p. 49–55) which gives the distribution of waiting time in a single server queue with any form of arrival and service distributions.

If $k(t)$ is the distribution of the difference, $t = v - u$, where v has the distribution of service time and u has the distribution of arrival intervals, then $W(t)$ the distribution of waiting time t is

$$W(t) = \int_{0^-}^{\infty} W(y)\, k(t-y)\, \mathrm{d}y \qquad (5.19)$$

This integral equation for $W(t)$ can be solved algebraically for some distributions of service and arrival, but its algebraic solution for the more useful forms of distribution is beyond the scope of this book. The solution can be found by an iterative numerical method for most practical distributions and it is for this approach a useful formula. Kendall[14] gives a simple derivation of the average waiting time for the queue $M/G/1$ which is quoted below.

Average waiting time in the queue $M/G/1$

$$= \frac{u \cdot s}{2(1-u)}\{1 + (\text{c.v.})^2\} \qquad (5.20)$$

where u = the utilisation of the system = $\dfrac{\text{average service time}}{\text{average arrival interval}}$

$\quad s$ = average service time

$(\text{c.v.})^2$ = variance of service time distribution$/s^2$

$\qquad$ = (coefficient of variation of service time)$^2 = v_s$

5.4 MULTI-SERVER QUEUES

While there are no results known to the author on the multi-server queue with any form of service and inter arrival distributions ($G/G/n$) results have been obtained for some multi-server queues with limitations on the form of only one of these distributions.

Kendall[1] shows that for the queue $G/M/n$ the distribution of waiting time will be negative exponential in form and gives a formula for the average of the distribution for those customers that have to wait.

$$W^*(t) = \text{distribution of waiting time for customers that have to wait}$$

$$= \frac{1}{c}\,e^{-t/c} \qquad (5.21)$$

where $c = \dfrac{s}{n(1-\lambda)}$

$s = $ average service time

and λ is given by

$$\lambda = F(\lambda) = \int_0^\infty e^{-(1-\lambda)nu/s}\,g(u)\,\mathrm{d}u \qquad (5.22)$$

where $g(t)$ is distribution function of inter arrival times.

The distribution $W^*(t)$ can be found easily for a wide range of arrival distributions. This result applies only to customers that have to wait and it is necessary to find the chance a customer does not have to wait to complete the study of queueing for all customers. The formulae for the probability a customer does not have to wait are difficult to evaluate for distributions of arrivals other than the distributions negative exponential and deterministic. Both these special cases have been covered in previous chapters.

Steady state probability equations for the queue $E_k/E_l/n$ can be written down and solved numerically, in a similar manner as for the special case $n = 1$, already covered. This makes use of the property that the Erlang distribution is the sum of several 'phases' each of which has a negative exponential distribution. The steady state equations will involve probabilities of the form $P(m, n_1, n_2, \ldots, n_l; j)$ where m is the number of 'phases' of the arrival distribution E_k the next arrival still has to complete, n_i is the number of customers which still have i phases of the service time to complete, and j is the number of customers in the system.

If $j < n$ $\Sigma n_i = j$,

and if $j \geqslant n$ $\Sigma n_i = n$.

J. O. Mayhugh and R. E. McCormick[15] have obtained numerical results for the case $M/E_3/2$; $u = 0\cdot3, 0\cdot6, 0\cdot9$. The average waiting time for customers in the queue can be found easily once the probabilities are known. The probabilities are of the form $P(n; x_3, x_2, x_1) = $ the chance there are n customers in the system, with x_j servers still having j phases of service to complete $x_3 + x_2 + x_1 = 2$. If $W(n; x_3, x_2, x_1)$ is defined as the average waiting time of a customer arriving to find the system in the state n; x_3, x_2, x_1 then the overall waiting time is

$$W = \Sigma P(n; x_3, x_2, x_1) \times W(n; x_3, x_2, x_1)$$

The conditional waiting times can be found since each service phase has a negative exponential distribution with an average of one third of the service time, in units of service time.

If $n < 2$ $W(n; x_3, x_2, x_1) = 0$.

$\qquad\qquad W(2; 0, 0, 2) \quad = \frac{1}{6}$.

$\qquad\qquad W(2; 0, 1, 1) \quad = \frac{1}{6} + \frac{1}{2} W(1; 0, 0, 1)$
$\qquad\qquad\qquad\qquad\qquad + \frac{1}{2} W(2; 0, 0, 2) = \frac{1}{4}$

$\qquad\qquad W(2; 1, 0, 1) \quad = \frac{1}{6} + \frac{1}{2} W(2; 0, 1, 1)$
$\qquad\qquad\qquad\qquad\qquad + \frac{1}{2} W(1; 1, 0, 0) = \frac{7}{24}$

$\qquad\qquad W(2; 0, 2, 0) \quad = \frac{1}{6} + W(2; 0, 1, 1) = \frac{5}{12}$
$\qquad\qquad\qquad\text{etc.}$

Since the right hand side of the equations involve values which have already been calculated the values of the conditional waiting times can be found for all states and hence W evaluated. When this is done using the values of $P(n; x_3, x_2, x_1)$ given in Mayhugh and McCormick[15] the average waiting time becomes as shown in Table 5.2.
It is interesting to compare these figures with those found by interpolating between the results for $M/M/2$ and $M/D/2$ in proportion to v_s,

the square of the coefficient of variation of the service time (see Table 5.3). For $M/E_3/2$ the square of the coefficient of variaton is $\frac{1}{3}$.

The error in the average waiting time obtained by simple interpolation can be seen to be small for practical purposes.

Table 5.2.

u	W
0·3	0·0679
0·6	0·3826
0·9	2·8888

Table 5.3. AVERAGE WAITING TIME (IN UNITS OF SERVICE TIME)

Utilisation	(M/D/2)	(M/M/2)	Estimate for* M/E₃/2	Actual M/E₃/2	% Error of Estimate
0·3	0·0553	0·0989	0·0698	0·0679	−2·7
0·6	0·2930	0·5625	0·3828	0·3826	+0·1
0·9	2·0138	4·2632	2·7636	2·8888	−4·3

* The estimate is obtained by linear interpolation, Estimate = $\frac{1}{3}$(M/M/2)+$\frac{2}{3}$(M/D/2)

5.4.1 Approximations to the value of Average Waiting Time in $E_k/E_l/n$

As in the single server queue the extreme cases of the queue $E_k/E_l/n$ in the form of distribution are $k, l = 1$ and ∞ giving the negative exponential and deterministic distributions respectively. The combinations of these extreme cases being $M/M/n$, $D/M/n$, $M/D/n$, and $D/D/n$. Since there is no waiting in the queue $D/D/n$ all these extreme cases have already been studied and results obtained for average waiting time. For the single server case linear interpolation on v_a and v_s gave reasonable approximations to the actual waiting time for $E_k/E_l/1$ from the four extreme cases. A similar approximation is attempted here.

Let $W_n(v_a, v_s, u) =$ the average waiting time in $E_k/E_l/n$ with utilisation u where $v_a = k^{-1}$ and $v_s = l^{-1}$
then

$W_n(1, 1, u) =$ the average waiting time in $M/M/n$ with utilisation u

$W_n(0, 1, u) =$ the average waiting time in $D/M/n$ with utilisation u

$W_n(1, 0, u) =$ the average waiting time in $M/D/n$ with utilisation u

$W_n(0, 0, u) =$ the average waiting time in $D/D/n$ with utilisation u

all the waiting times being measured in units of service time.
Assuming linear interpolation on v_a and v_s is valid the average waiting time in the general case will be given by

$$W_n(v_a, v_s, u) = (1-v_a)(1-v_s) W_n(0, 0, u) + (1-v_a) v_s W_n(0, 1, u)$$
$$+ (1-v_s) v_a W_n(1, 0, u) + v_a v_s W_n(1, 1, u)$$

since $W_n(0, 0, u) = 0$ this becomes

$$W_n(v_a, v_s, u) = (1-v_a) v_s W_n(0, 1, u) + v_a(1-v_s) W_n(1, 0, u)$$
$$+ v_a v_s W_n(1, 1, u) \qquad (5.23)$$

The approximation can be tested at values of v_a and v_s other than 0 or 1. Since $v_a = v_s = \frac{1}{2}$ is the central point in the area of the v_a, v_s plane being considered, the exact values of waiting time are evaluated for this case. When $v_a = v_s = \frac{1}{2}$ then $l = k = 2$ and the queue becomes $E_2/E_2/n$. Since the formula relating waiting time to arrival rate and average number of customers in the queue holds, namely

Average waiting time $\times$ average arrival rate = average number in queue

Then once the average number of customers in the queue is known, the average waiting time is easily calculated. The average number of customers in the queue can be found from the steady state probabilities, which are derived below.

5.4.2 Steady State Probabilities for the queue $E_2/E_2/n$

Let $P(l, m; j) =$ the probability there are j customers in the system, m of the customers being served have only one 'phase' of service to complete before the end of service, and the next customer to arrive has l 'phases' of arrival interval to complete before arrival at the system.

l can take values 1 and 2.

m can take values from 0 to the minimum of j and n.

j can take any value from 0 to ∞.

If λ = the rate of movement from one arrival phase to the next = $2/a$ and μ = the rate of movement from one service phase to the next = = $2/s$

where a = the average arrival interval, and s = the average service time, then the equations for the probabilities are

$$\lambda P(1, 0; 0) = \lambda P(2, 0; 0) + \mu P(1, 1; 1)$$
$$\lambda P(2, 0, 0) = \mu P(2, 1; 1)$$
$$(\lambda + j\mu) P(1, m; j) = \lambda P(2, m; j) + (j - m + 1) \mu P(1, m - 1; j)$$
$$+ (m + 1) \mu P(1, m + 1; j + 1)$$
$$m = 1, 2, \ldots, j$$
$$j = 1, 2, \ldots, n - 1$$
$$(\lambda + j\mu) P(2, m; j) = \lambda P(1, m; j - 1) + (j - m + 1) \mu P(2, m - 1; j)$$
$$+ (m + 1) \mu P(2, m + 1; j + 1)$$
$$m = 1, 2, \ldots, j$$
$$j = 1, 2, \ldots, n - 1$$
$$(\lambda + j\mu) P(1, 0; j) = \lambda P(2, 0; j) + \mu P(1, 1; j + 1)$$
$$j = 1, 2, \ldots, n - 1$$
$$(\lambda + j\mu) P(2, 0; j) = \lambda P(1, 0; j - 1) + \mu P(2, 1; j + 1)$$
$$j = 1, 2, \ldots, n - 1$$
$$(\lambda + n\mu) P(l, m; j) = \lambda P(2, m; j) + (n - m + 1) \mu P(1, m - 1; j)$$
$$+ (m + 1) \mu P(1, m + 1; j + 1)$$
$$m = 1, 2, \ldots, n - 1$$
$$j = n, n + 1, \ldots, \infty$$
$$(\lambda + n\mu) P(2, m; j) = \lambda P(1, m; j - 1) + (n - m + 1) \mu P(2, m - 1; j)$$
$$+ (m + 1) \mu P(2, m + 1; j + 1)$$
$$m = 1, 2, \ldots, n - 1$$
$$j = n, n + 1, \ldots, \infty$$

$$(\lambda + n\mu)P(1, 0; j) = \lambda P(2, 0; j) + \mu P(1, 1; j+1)$$
$$j = n, n+1, \ldots, \infty$$
$$(\lambda + n\mu)P(2, 0; j) = \lambda P(1, 0; j-1) + \mu P(2, 1; j+1)$$
$$j = n, n+1, \ldots, \infty$$
$$(\lambda + n\mu)P(1, n; j) = \lambda P(2, n; j) + \mu P(1, n-1; j)$$
$$j = n, n+1, \ldots, \infty$$
$$(\lambda + n\mu)P(2, n; j) = \lambda P(1, n; j-1) + \mu P(2, n-1; j)$$
$$j = n, n+1, \ldots, \infty \tag{5.24}$$

These equations can be solved numerically and the average number of customers in the queue derived from the probabilities.
Let

$$Q(j) = \sum_m P(1, m; j) + \sum_m P(2, m; j) \tag{5.25}$$
$$j = 0, 1, 2, \ldots, \infty$$

then the average number in queue $= \sum_{j=n}^{\infty} (j-n)Q(j) \tag{5.26}$

The solution of the equations was obtained by an iterative process which gave the probabilities accurate to six decimal places at which point the average number in the queue was calculated. The process worked quite well on utilisations up to $u = 0.7$ but was rather slow for higher utilisations so estimates were found by simulation for the higher utilisations. The results are given in Table A.4.

5.4.3 Comparison between approximation and exact results for $E_2/E_2/n$

Using the approximation for average waiting time given in equation 5.23 for $v_a = v_s = 0.5$ the formula below is obtained.

$$W_n(\tfrac{1}{2}, \tfrac{1}{2}, u) = \tfrac{1}{4}\{W_n(0, 1, u) + W_n(1, 0; u) + W_n(1, 1, u)\} \tag{5.27}$$

$W_n(0, 1, u)$ is tabulated in Table A.3

$W_n(1, 0, u)$ is tabulated in Table A.2

and $W_n(1, 1, n)$ is tabulated in Table A.1. The approximation is easily calculated and the results are as shown in Table 5.4.

Table 5.4. ESTIMATE OF AVERAGE WAITING TIME IN $E_2/E_2/n$ USING LINEAR INTERPOLATION BETWEEN $D/D/n$; $M/D/n$; $D/M/n$; $M/M/n$

u	Number of Servers n								
	2	3	4	5	6	7	8	9	10
0·1	0·0041	0·0006	0·0001	0·0000	0·0000	0·0000	0·0000	0·0000	0·0000
0·2	0·0166	0·0042	0·0013	0·0004	0·0001	0·0000	0·0000	0·0000	0·0000
0·3	0·0398	0·0136	0·0055	0·0024	0·0012	0·0006	0·0003	0·0001	0·0001
0·4	0·0790	0·0324	0·0156	0·0083	0·0046	0·0027	0·0016	0·0010	0·0007
0·5	0·1437	0·0673	0·0368	0·0219	0·0138	0·0092	0·0062	0·0043	0·0030
0·6	0·2519	0·1306	0·0785	0·0512	0·0353	0·0253	0·0186	0·0140	0·0108
0·7	0·4450	0·2507	0·1622	0·1135	0·0835	0·0637	0·0499	0·0399	0·0324
0·8	0·8480	0·5110	·3510	0·2595	0·2010	0·1610	0·1321	0·1104	0·0937
0·9	2·0525	1·3509	0·9411	0·7264	0·5855	0·4872	0·4141	0·3581	0·3141

As can be seen by comparing the table of approximations with the exact results the approximation is usually accurate to the first or second decimal place. The percentage error is smallest at higher utilisations as was the case for the single server comparisons. The approximation is always an overestimate of the actual queueing, the error being as low as 3% at high utilisation rising to about 20% at utilisation of 0·6. From a practical viewpoint the approximation is useful since its error is small at the higher utilisations which are more likely to be met in actual queueing situations.

Example 5.3

Data on lorry arrivals at a works weighbridge show that the average arrival interval is 10·4 min and its standard deviation is 2·3 min. On being served a lorry occupies one weighing platform exclusively for 32 min on average with a standard deviation of 7 min. If it costs as much to keep a lorry waiting for service as it does to provide a platform for the same length of time, how many weighing platforms should be installed at the weighbridge?

$$v_a = \text{(s.d. of arrivals/mean arrival)}^2 = (2\cdot3/10\cdot4)^2 = 0\cdot0489$$

$$v_s = \text{(s.d. of service time/mean service time)}^2 = (7/32)^2 = 0\cdot479$$

Arrival rate/service rate $= 32/10\cdot4 = 3\cdot08$ so at least 4 platforms are required. Taking $n = 4, 5$ etc. in turn
$n = 4$ utilisation $= 0\cdot7692$
at utilisation 0·7 equation 5.23 gives.

$$
\begin{aligned}
W_4(0\cdot0489, 0\cdot0479, 0\cdot7) &= 0\cdot9511\times0\cdot0479W_4(0, 1, 0\cdot7)\\
&\quad +0\cdot0489\times0\cdot9521W_4(1, 0, 0\cdot7)\\
&\quad +0\cdot0489\times0\cdot0479W_4(1, 1, 0\cdot7)\\
&= 0\cdot0456\times0\cdot1020+0\cdot0466\times0\cdot1897\\
&\quad +0\cdot0023\times0\cdot3572 = 0\cdot0143
\end{aligned}
$$

similarly
$$
\begin{aligned}
W_4(0\cdot0489, 0\cdot0479, 0\cdot8) &= 0\cdot0456\times0\cdot2725+0\cdot0466\times0\cdot386\\
&\quad +0\cdot0023\times0\cdot7455 = 0\cdot0321
\end{aligned}
$$

interpolating on $\log_{L} W$ for intermediate value of u gives
$$W_4(0\cdot0489, 0\cdot0479. 0\cdot7692) = 0\cdot0250$$

Taking the unit cost as the cost of running a platform for one hour the hourly costs with 4 platforms $= 4 + $ arrivals/hour $\times W_4 \times$ average service time in hours

$$= 4 + 5 \cdot 77 \times 0 \cdot 025 \, 0 \times 32/60 = 4 \cdot 076 \, 9$$

Obviously the running cost with 5 platforms will be at least 5 units per hour which is higher than the total cost when 4 platforms are operated so 4 is the optimum number of platforms to use in this case. The error in using the approximate waiting time formula (equation 5.23) is not going to be large enough to alter the decision in this case since it would mean the waiting time cost estimated at $0 \cdot 0769$ would have to be as large as $1 \cdot 0$ before the decision was changed. The errors in waiting time are not as large as the ratio of these figures at any point of the tables and so the result is valid.

Example 5.4

Three locomotives are continuously available in a steelworks to move trains of bogies within the works. Demands for movement occur every $3 \cdot 7$ min on average with a standard deviation of $2 \cdot 4$ min. The time to move a train takes $9 \cdot 7$ min on average with a s.d. of 7 min. How many minutes does a train have to wait for a locomotive on average?

$$v_a = \text{(s.d. of arrival/mean arrival interval)}^2 = (2 \cdot 4/3 \cdot 7)^2 = 0 \cdot 420 \, 7$$

$$v_s = \text{(s.d. of service time/mean service time)}^2 = (7/9 \cdot 7)^2 = 0 \cdot 520 \, 8$$

$n = 3$, utilisation $= \dfrac{9 \cdot 7}{3 \times 3 \cdot 7} = 0 \cdot 873 \, 9$

using equation 5.23

$$
\begin{aligned}
W_3(0 \cdot 420 \, 7, \, 0 \cdot 520 \, 8, \, 0 \cdot 9) &= 0 \cdot 579 \, 3 \times 5 \cdot 520 \, 8 \times W_3(0, \, 1, \, 0 \cdot 9) \\
&\quad + 0 \cdot 420 \, 7 \times 0 \cdot 479 \, 2 \times W_3(1, \, 0, \, 0 \cdot 9) \\
&\quad + 0 \cdot 420 \, 7 \times 0 \cdot 520 \, 8 \times W_3(1, \, 1, \, 0 \cdot 9) \\
&= 0 \cdot 301 \, 7 \times 1 \cdot 121 \, 2 + 0 \cdot 201 \, 6 \times 1 \cdot 288 \, 7 \\
&\quad + 0 \cdot 219 \, 1 \times 2 \cdot 723 \, 5 = 1 \cdot 221 \, 9
\end{aligned}
$$

similarly $W_3(0.420\,7, 0.520\,8, 0.8) = 0.301\,7 \times 0.411\,4 + 0.201\,6 \times 0.553.7$
$$+ 0.219\,1 \times 1.078\,7 = 0.472\,1$$
interpolating for u

$$W_3(0.420\,7, 0.520\,8, 0.873\,9) = 0.956\,0$$

Average waiting time $= 0.956\,0 \times$ average service time
$$= 0.956\,0 \times 9.7 \text{ min}$$
$$= \underline{9.3 \text{ min}}$$

5.5 PROBLEMS

1. Using the formula 5.23 giving an approximate value of waiting time in the multi-server queue, find the optimum number of berths required at a port where the following information is available.

The average interval between arrival of ships is 2·1 h, with s.d. = 1·5 h. The berth time of ships has an average of 11·9 h with s.d. = 1·2 h. The cost of installing and running a berth is £1 000 per day and the cost of keeping a ship waiting is £500 per day.

2. A company employs a number of fork lift trucks for movement of materials within its factory. The calls for use of the trucks occur every 10·9 min on average with a standard deviation of 2·6 min. The time a truck is engaged with a call is 25 min on average with s.d. = 7·4 min. Three trucks are continuously available for this work. What is the average delay to calls because they are waiting for a truck?

The factory is being expanded and the calls are expected to increase to a rate of one every 8·7 min on average with the same s.d. as before. There is no change in the time a truck is occupied with a call. How many extra trucks are needed if the delays are not to be longer on average than previously?

3. A port has one berth capable of unloading vessels importing bulk cargo. Vessels arrive on average every twelve hours in a Poisson stream. The unloading facilities at the berth can be improved to reduce the unloading time if necessary. If an average unloading time of m hours is maintained the weekly running costs of such facilities are £113,400/m. The distribution of unloading times is Erlang with $v_s = 0.5$. The present average unloading time is 10 h. Penalties are paid

by the port authorities to the ship owners if ships are kept waiting, these being £100 per ship hour of delay. What is the best average unloading time?

4. Two servers are available to serve customers who arrive at random at an average rate of one a minute. The service time has an Erlang distribution with mean $1\frac{1}{3}$ min and standard deviation $2\sqrt{2}/3$ min. The service system is modified so that each server specialises in a particular type of service. Under the new system one server receives customers at random at a rate 2 every 3 min and the service time is 1 min on average with standard deviation $1/\sqrt{2}$ min and has an Erlang distribution. The second server receives customers at a rate of 1 every 3 min at random. The service time of the second server has an Erlang distribution with average 2 min and standard deviation $\sqrt{2}$ min. Which system gives the lower waiting time averaged over all customers?

CHAPTER 6

Machine Interference

6.1 INTRODUCTION

The customers in many queueing systems in industry are the same men or machines repeatedly requiring the same form of service. The earliest problem of this type to be studied extensively was that of a batch of production machines subject to breakdown, which were then repaired by an operative. The practical problem is to decide how many machines should be under the attention of an operative, or alternatively, how many operatives are needed to tend a given batch of machines.

The factors affecting the solution of the problem are the running time of the machines before breakdown and the time taken by the operative to repair the machine. Both these factors are variable to a greater or lesser extent in practice so there are occasions when more than one machine will require the services of the operative at the same time. Since the operative can repair only one machine at a time, some machines will be delayed in their repair because others are taking the operatives attention at the time of break down. This has resulted in the type of problem being called a *machine interference* problem.

Because of the variability in either repair time, or running time, or both, these will each have a distribution. The amount of delay machines will incur depends on

1. The number of machines the operative has to attend.
2. The distribution of running time of the machines.
3. The distribution of repair time by the operative.

The machines are usually of the same type and have identical distributions of running time, and their repair times are also identical in a statistical sense, so only two distributions, 2 and 3, are required and not two for each machine in the batch tended by the operative.

The solution to the practical problem is an economic balance of the cost of providing operatives against the profit on production from the machines. The production from the machines, or the average number of machines running is required for this cost analysis. The method of operation of a batch of machines is usually either to divide the batch into equal groups and each group tended by one operative or to have the whole batch tended by all operatives. The production, or average number of machines running in a group tended by one or many operatives is of interest in finding the solution to the practical problem. The study of these problems is divided into these two types, groups of machines with a single operative and groups with many operatives.

6.2 MACHINES UNDER THE ATTENTION OF ONE OPERATIVE

The factors of interest in this case are usually the average number of machines running, and the proportion of time the operative will be idle. The cycle of a machine is divided into three parts, running or production time, (p), delay for repair, (d), and repair time (r). The utilisation of a machine (E) is the proportion of time it will be in production, or running, i.e.

$$E = p/(p+d+r) \tag{6.1}$$

If the number of machines under the attention of the operative is N, then

$$\text{The average number of machines running} = A = NE \tag{6.2}$$

The proportion of time the operative will be busy in each machine cycle is $r/(p+d+r)$, since there are N machines keeping the operative busy for the same proportion of time.

$$\text{The operative utilisation } (P) = N \cdot r/(p+d+r) \tag{6.3}$$

which gives

$$P = (r/p) \, Np/(p+d+r) = (r/p)NE = A(r/p)$$

if $r/p = x$

$$P = Ax \tag{6.4}$$

Once either the average number of machines running, or the operative utilisation, is calculated this relationship can be used to find the other. Since no assumption has been made about the form of distributions of repair and running time in the derivation of equation 6.4 this applies to all cases with a single operative. The average number of machines running can be found from the probabilities of the number of machines running at any time, so most of the mathematical work is aimed at calculating these probabilities. These depend on the form of distribution of the repair and running time. Results are known for several forms of distribution, which are considered in turn below.

6.2.1 Negative Exponential Distributions of Repair and Running Times

This case was considered by Feller[16], the average rate of repair is $\mu = 1$/average repair time, and the average running time is $1/\lambda$. The equations for the time dependent probabilities,

$P_t(j)$ = the probability at time t there are j machines broken down

can be written down as for the queue $M/M/n$ and a steady state solution shown to exist. The steady state probabilities,

$P(j)$ = the chance there are j machines broken down can be found from the steady state equations.

$$((\mu + (N-j)\lambda) P(j) = \mu P(j+1) + (N-j+1) \lambda P(j-1) \tag{6.5}$$
$$j = 1, 2, \ldots, N-1$$
$$\mu P(N) = \lambda P(N-1)$$

which gives

$$P(j) = \left(\frac{\lambda}{\mu}\right)^j \frac{N!}{(N-j)!} P(0) \tag{6.6}$$
$$j = 1, 2, \ldots, N$$

since $\sum_{j=0}^{I} P(j) = 1$

$$P(0)^{-1} = \sum_{j=0}^{N} \frac{x^j N!}{(N-j)!}$$

where $x = \dfrac{\lambda}{\mu} = \dfrac{\text{average repair time}}{\text{average running time}}$

The chance the operative is idle = the chance no machines are broken down = $P(0)$.

The average number of machines running is

$$A_i = \sum_{j=0}^{N-1} (N-j) P(j) = \sum_{j=0}^{N-1} (N-j) \frac{x^j N!}{(N-j)!} P(0) = \sum_{j=0}^{N-1} \frac{x^j N!}{(N-j-1)!} P(0)$$

Benson and Cox[17] define $F(x, N) = \sum_{j=0}^{N} x^j N!/(N-j)!$

which gives
$$P(0) = F(x, N)^{-1} \tag{6.7}$$
$$A = N \cdot F(x, N-1)/F(x, N) \tag{6.8}$$

it is easy to show
$$F(x, N) = 1 + NxF(x, N-1) \tag{6.9}$$
$$N > 0$$

and
$$F(x, 0) = 1$$

Using these equations it is easy to evaluate the values $P(0)$, and A for a specified value of x for increasing values of N.

Example 6.1

A plant in continuous production consists of a batch of 60 machines. Breakdowns to the machines occur at random with an average running time before breakdown of 20 min. Repair time has a negative exponential distribution with an average of 3 min. The allocation of machines to operatives is made by dividing the 60 machines equally between the operatives available. Each operative is responsible for repairs on her share of the batch. Profit on one machine hour's running time is £2, and the cost of providing one operative continuously is £70, per week. How many operatives should be made available to tend to the machines?

$x = 3/20 = 0.15$

The net profit is largest when the number of machines per operative is 3 so 20 operatives are needed to tend the 60 machines (see Table 6.1). Operative utilisation with 20 operatives

$$P = Nx \ \text{(Machine utilisation)}$$
$$= 37.7\%$$

Table 6.1.

N	Nx	F(x, n)	Machine utilisation	Profit (£)	Operative cost (£)	Difference (£)
0	0	1·000 00				
1	0·15	1·150 00	0·869 565	17 530	4 200	13 330
2	0·30	1·345 00	0·855 019	17 237	2 100	15 137
3	0·45	1·605 25	0·837 876	16 892	1 400	15 492
4	0·60	1·963 150	0·817 691	16 485	1 050	15 435

Benson and Cox[17] tabulate the operative utilisation, P, for values of $N = 1$, (1), 15 and $x = 0·10$, (0·01), 0·20, (0·10), 1·00. Cox[18] has compressed the tables so that large values of N can be considered by using Nx, and x as the entries to the tables instead of N and x. The values covered are

$Nx \quad = 0·1$, (0·1), 0·8, (0·05), 1·2, (0·1), 1·5;

$x \quad\quad = 0·005$, (0·001), 0·01, (0·01), 0·04,

and $Nx = 0·1$, (0·1), 1·9; $x = 0·04$, (0·01), 0·12

6.2.2 Constant Repair Time, Negative Exponential Running Time

This model is closer to most practical situations than the previous model. The repair on many machines consists of the same operation, so little variation in the repair time would be expected. Most of the early work on machine interference is applied to spinning machines where the repair is the joining of yarn which has broken; so the operative is likely to take roughly the same time on each repair. Ashcroft[19] produced the solution to the more general model with any distribution of repair time and negative exponential distribution of running time.

If

$$p(t) = \text{the p.d.f. of repair time } t$$

and A_k, f_k, Y_N are defined as:

$$A_k = \int_0^\infty e^{-kt} p(t) \, \mathrm{d}t; \quad f_k = A_k^{-1} - 1$$

$$k = 1, 2, \ldots$$

$$Y_N = 1 + \sum_{r=1}^{N-1} \binom{N-1}{r} \prod_{k=1}^{r} f_k$$

then Ashcroft's solution for machine utilisation, E, is:

$$E = Y_N (1 + NxY_N)^{-1} \tag{6.10}$$

hence average number of machines running $= A = NE$

For the special case of constant repair time, Ashcroft produced tables of A for a range of values of N and x (p in Ashcroft's notation), these being

$$N = 1, \quad (1), \quad 6; \quad x = 0\cdot00, \ (0\cdot01), \ 0\cdot35, \ (0\cdot05), \ 1\cdot00$$
$$N = 7, \quad (1), \quad 10; \quad x = 0\cdot00, \ (0\cdot01), \ 0\cdot54$$
$$N = 11, \quad (1), \quad 20; \quad x = 0\cdot00, \ (0\cdot005), \ 0\cdot15, \ (0\cdot01), \ 0\cdot27$$

Example 6.2

Taking the same example as before with the repair time constant instead of negative exponential, and using Ashcroft's tables one finds $x = 0\cdot15$

Table 6.2.

N	A	E	Profit ($£$)	Operative Cost ($£$)	Difference ($£$)
1	0·869 6	0·869 6	17 530	4 200	13 330
2	1·723 1	0·861 6	17 369	2 100	15 269
3	2·554 3	0·851 4	17 165	1 400	15 765
4	3·354 1	0·838 5	16 905	1 050	15 855
5	4·109 1	0·821 8	16 568	840	15 728

The optimum machines per operative is now 4 giving 15 as the number of operatives for the batch (see Table 6.2). The removal of variation in repair time has decreased the interference between machines and enabled higher machine utilisations with corresponding numbers of operatives. Tables of utilisation for constant repair time and negative exponential running time for a larger range of machines under the care of the operative than the table in Ashcroft's paper are given in Anson[20] which cover

$$N = 2, (1), 50; \quad x = 0.10, (0.01), 0.20, (0.10), 1.00$$

6.2.3 Negative Exponential Repair Time, Erlang Running Time

In attempting to obtain utilisations for a more general distribution than the two considered above, Benson[21] studied the case of negative exponential repair times and running time of the Erlang form. The probabilities, $P(j)$, of there being j machines broken down are found to be identical to the case with negative exponential running and repair times. Hence the utilisations will also be identical to that case. The distribution of running time in this case is irrelevant, it has not yet been shown to be true for any distribution of running time to the author's knowledge but it would appear reasonable to assume any effect of the form of the distribution on the results will be small.

6.2.4 General Repair Time, Negative Exponential Running Time

This case is considered by Ashcroft[19], Cox[22] suggests an approximation to the machine utilisation in this case is a linear interpolation between the case with constant repair time and the case with negative exponential repair time; the interpolation being in proportion to the square of the coefficient of variation of the repair time. The linear interpolation is usually accurate to two decimal places but corrections are given in Cox[22] to give higher accuracy if required. This is useful since tables are available for the two extreme cases in Ashcroft[19] for constant repair, and Anson[20] or Benson and Cox[17] for negative exponential repair times.

6.3 MACHINES UNDER THE CARE OF SEVERAL OPERATIVES

The operation of a group of machines by dividing it into shares each allocated to a single operative is inefficient in some respects. It is possible for operatives on some shares to be unoccupied when machines in other shares are awaiting repair. An alternative method is to allow any operative to repair any machine, which should reduce the interference between machines. In practice it may be that the time taken by the operatives to move from one machine to the next requiring repair is of the same order as the repair time. The pooling of operatives to tend any machine will usually increase the time to move, compared with the single operative share system. If this increase is sufficiently large it could outweigh the advantages of reduced interference in the pooled system. When the movement time is included as part of the repair time the correct utilisations will be obtained.

6.3.1 Mathematical Development for Negative Exponential Repair and Running Times

If the number of machines in the group is N, the number of operatives tending the machines is m, the average repair time is $1/\mu$, and the average running time $1/\lambda$, then the steady state probabilities $P(j)$ of there being j machines broken down are given by the equations

$$\left.\begin{aligned}
N\lambda P(0) &= \mu P(1) \\
((N-j)\,\lambda+j\mu)\,P(j) &= (j+1)\,\mu P(j+1)+(N-j+1)\,\lambda P(j-1) \\
&\qquad 1 \leqslant j < m \\
((N-j)\lambda+m\mu)\,P(j) &= m\mu P(j+1)+(N-j+1)\,\lambda P(j-1) \\
&\qquad m \leqslant j < N \\
m\mu P(N) &= \lambda P(N-1)
\end{aligned}\right\} \quad (6.11)$$

which give solutions $P(j) = \dbinom{N}{j}\left(\dfrac{\lambda}{\mu}\right)^{j} P(0),\; j \leqslant m$

$$P(j) = \frac{N!}{m!\,(N-j)!}\;\frac{1}{m^{j-m}}\left(\frac{\lambda}{\mu}\right)^{j} P(0), \qquad N \geqslant j \geqslant m$$

summing the probabilities to unity gives $P(0)$ and hence all the probabilities. The operative and machine utilisations can now be determined.

Average number of machines running $= \Sigma(N-j)P(j) = A$

Machine utilisation $= A/N = E$

Average number of repairs $= \sum_{j=0}^{m-1} jP(j) + m\sum_{m}^{N} P(j) = R$

Operative utilisation $= P = R/m$

The values of the chance a machine is delayed for repair, and the machine utilisation are given in Peck and Hazelwood[23] for a range of values of m, N and X where

$X = $ (repair time)/(repair time + running time)

The range of values of m for any particular value of N and X was determined by the variation of the number of machines being repaired when $m = N$. To a rough approximation this will be a binomial distribution with mean NX and standard deviation $(NX(1-X))^{1/2}$. The range of m is then taken from one to four standard deviations above the mean, i.e.

$$m = 1, 2, \ldots, NX + 4[NX(1-X)]^{1/2}$$

The ranges of N and X are:

$N = 4, (1), 26;$ $X = 0\cdot001, (0\cdot001), 0\cdot026,$

$N = 26, (2), 70;$ $X = 0\cdot026, (0\cdot002), 0\cdot070,$

$N = 70, (5), 170;$ $X = 0\cdot070, (0\cdot005), 0\cdot170,$

$N = 170, (10);$ $X = 0\cdot170, (0\cdot010), 0\cdot340,$

$X = 0\cdot340; (0\cdot020), 0\cdot600,$

$X = 0\cdot600; (0\cdot050), 0\cdot950,$

Example 6.3

Ingots of steel are heated to the temperature required for rolling in soaking pits. The time taken to heat the ingots is very variable and can be assumed to have a negative exponential distribution. There is one rolling mill which reduces the ingots to slabs. The time taken to roll the ingots from a soaking pit is constant. On continuous working sufficient pits must be provided to ensure that the mill is not delayed by more than one hour a week on average because there are no ingots ready to roll in the soaking pits. The average time to heat a pit of ingots to be ready for rolling is 3 h. The time taken to roll the ingots in a pit is 20 min. What is the smallest number of soaking pits needed to provide the specified utilisation of the mill?

Treating the mill as the operative, and the pits as machines, the problem becomes a machine interference problem with constant repair time of 20 min (the rolling time for a pit) and exponential running time (the heating time). A single operative (the mill), looks after the machines, and the requirement is that the operative must be busy for not less than $167/168 = 99 \cdot 40\%$ of the time. Results for this model are tabulated in Ashcroft[19], the value of x is $x =$ repair time/running time $= 20/180 = 0 \cdot 111$ which gives from the tables the values in Table 6.3 The lowest value of N which gives an operative utilisation higher than $0 \cdot 9940$ is 15, which is the number of soaking pits required.

Table 6.3.

N	A	$P = Ax$
7	5·949 1	0·661 0
10	7·856 0	0·872 9
12	8·612 5	0·956 9
13	8·816 1	0·979 6
14	8·928 7	0·992 1
15	8·981 5	0·997 9

Example 6.4

A steel works aims to keep 20 ladles in operation to transport molten iron from the blast furnaces to the steel making plants. Since ladles must go out of operation from time to time for repair a number of spare ladles are required to maintain the required number in service. The repair policy is to have one repair crew working if there are two or more spare ladles ready to go into operation when required, and to have two repair crews working when there are less than two spare ladles ready to go into operation. A repair crew repairs one ladle at a time. Both time in operation and repair times have negative exponential distributions, the average time in operation is 42 days and the average repair time is 3 days.

If $P(j)$ is the steady state probability of there being j ladles either in service or ready to go into service, the equations with N ladles in the system are, with $\lambda =$ breakdown rate, $\mu =$ repair rate of one crew:

$$2\mu P(0) = \lambda P(1)$$
$$(2\mu + j\lambda)P(j) = (j+1)\lambda P(j+1) + 2\mu P(j-1)$$
$$j = 1, 2, \ldots, 19$$

$$(2\mu + 20\lambda)P(20) = 20\lambda P(21) + 2\mu P(19)$$
$$(2\mu + 20\lambda)P(21) = 20\lambda P(22) + 2\mu P(20)$$
$$(\mu + 20\lambda)P(22) = 20\lambda P(23) + 2\mu P(21)$$
$$(\mu + 20\lambda)P(j) = 20\lambda P(j+1) + \mu P(j-1)$$
$$j = 23, 24, \ldots, N-1$$
$$20\lambda P(N) = \mu P(N-1)$$

the solution of these equations is straightforward and the probability of not being able to maintain 20 ladles in operation, $\sum_{j=0}^{19} P(j)$ can be found by summation. The numerical results are as shown in Table 6.4.

Table 6.4. SECOND CREW TAKEN OFF IF 2 OR MORE LADLES READY FOR OPERATION

Number of Ladles in System	20	21	22	23	24	25	30	35	40
Chance of not having 20 Ladles in Operation (%)	65.7	44.4	30.5	25.1	22.3	20.7	18.1	17.7	17.7

No matter how large the number of ladles in the system the chance of having 20 ladles in operation never drops below 17·7%. The probability can be decreased by changing the conditions for having two repair crews available. If two crews work when there are less than 3 ladles ready to go into operation, and one crew when 3 or more are ready, the results become as shown in Table 6.5.

Table 6.5. SECOND CREW TAKEN OFF WHEN 3 OR MORE LADLES READY

Number of Ladles in System	20	21	22	23	24	25	30	35	40
Chance of not having 20 Ladles in Operation (%)	65.7	44.4	30.5	21.3	17.5	15.6	12.9	12.5	12.4

The chance of not having the required number of ladles in operation has now dropped for corresponding numbers of ladles in the system to the previous case. By repeating the calculations for a range of values of the number of ladles in the system and alternative crew availability rules it is possible to find combinations which will give an acceptably low chance of not having 20 ladles in operation. The choice of which one of these feasible combinations to take can then be made on a cost analysis. The extreme case where two crews are always available gives the results shown in Table 6.6 showing that the retention of two repair crews has more effect in this case than increasing the number of ladles in the system to a great extent. The results in the general case will depend on the ratio of repair time to time in operation so no general statement on the relative advantages of more ladles compared with more crews can be made.

Table 6.6.

Number of Ladles in System	20	21	22	23	24	25	30	35
Chance of not having 20 Ladles in Operation (%)	65.7	44.4	30.5	21.3	14.9	10.5	1.9	0.0

6.4 PROBLEMS

1. A group of 6 machines is tended by 3 operators. The machines break down on average every half hour and the distribution of running time is negative exponential. The machines take 45 min to repair on average and the distribution of repair time is also negative exponential. What are the steady state probabilities for the number of machines in use and what is the most likely number of machines in use? What is the average number of machines in use?

2. Two mechanics deal with the repairs of a group of seven machines. The repair and running times both have negative exponential distributions. The average running time is one hour and the average repair time is half an hour. By how much would the average number of machines running drop if one of the machines was taken out of production?

3. Four operatives tend seven machines whose repair and running times have negative exponential distributions with means of 5 min and 10 min respectively.

The operatives find by working in teams of two the repair time can be cut to two minutes on average, still with a negative exponential distribution. What are the machine utilisations under each system of operation?

4. How many operatives should be employed to perform repairs on a batch of six machines for which the following data is available?

The machines are in operation continuously except when broken down or under repair. Running times and repair times both have negative exponential distributions with means of 60 min and 20 min respectively. Profit on production is £2 per machine running hour, and it costs £100 per week to have one operative continuously available to repair the machines.

5. The demand for the product from a machine shop is expanding and the number of machines is to be increased to meet the expected demand. Figures for both these are given in Table 6.7.

The production rate of a machine is 100 units per hour of running time. Both repair and running time have negative exponential distributions with averages of 10 min and 40 min respectively. The number of operatives continuously available is planned to be 2 in 1970 and 3 in subsequent years. Any operative is able to repair any machine. Show that with the planned number of operatives and machines, it is possible to meet the expected demand and give the amounts by which the expected will be exceeded.

Table 6.7.

Year	1970	1971	1972	1973	1974
Expected hourly demand	350	395	430	470	550
Number of machines	5	5	6	6	7

CHAPTER 7

Finite Queues or Queues with Limited Waiting Room

7.1. INTRODUCTION

Much of the early work on queues was applied to telephone systems where the customers are subscribers requiring the use of local or trunk lines. A subscriber finding all the lines engaged cannot be held until a line becomes free and his call is lost. The study of telephone systems to keep the number of lost calls below acceptable limits and yet not have too much idle capacity in the system was the aim of this early work.

This is an extreme example of a queue with limited waiting room, in this case there is no waiting allowed at all. Customers arriving to find all lines in use are turned away. A new factor becomes of interest in such a queueing system, the chance a customer is turned away. A similar system is a car park, if there is room for a car to park the car is accepted otherwise the car is turned away.

In the terms of queueing theory the servers in these examples are the trunk lines, or local lines, and the spaces in the car park. The system can still be described by the inter arrival distribution, the service time distribution and the number of servers in the system but an additional factor is now required to complete the description, the maximum number of custmers that may be queueing at any time.

Most practical queueing problems have a limit to the number of customers that may queue at any one time. The limit may be much larger than any likely size of the queue, in which case the results for the infinite queues studied in previous chapters are valid. If the limit is below the size the queue may build up to then a separate study with the limit introduced must be made.

The mathematical development of the queues with limited waiting room is almost exactly parallel to the similar queue without a limit on the queue size and so only an outline of the mathematical method will be given for each case studied.

7.2. MATHEMATICAL DEVELOPMENT FOR QUEUES WITH LIMITED WAITING ROOM

7.2.1 The Queue $M/M/n$ with a Maximum of N Customers in the Queue

The equations for the steady state probabilities are found by the same method as for the queue $M/M/n$ with no limit on the queue size, the only change being in the equation for $P(n+N)$. If λ is the arrival rate of the customers, and μ the service rate of individual servers then the equations are

$$\lambda P(0) = \mu P(1)$$
$$(\lambda + j\mu) P(j) = (j+1)\,\mu P(j+1) + \lambda P(j-1) \qquad (7.1)$$
$$1 \leqslant j < n$$
$$(\lambda + n\mu) P(j) = n\mu P(j+1) + \lambda P(j-1)$$
$$n \leqslant j < N+n$$
$$n\mu P(N+n) = \lambda P(N+n-1)$$

the solutions are

$$\left. \begin{aligned} P(j) &= \frac{x^j}{j!}\,P(0) & j \leqslant n \\[2mm] P(j) &= \frac{x^j}{n!\,n^{j-n}}\,P(0) & j \geqslant n \end{aligned} \right\} \qquad (7.2)$$

$$x = \lambda/\mu$$

since $\sum_{j=0}^{N+n} P(j) = 1$

$$P(0)^{-1} = \sum_{j=0}^{n-1} \frac{x^j}{j!} + \frac{x^n}{n!} \sum_{k=0}^{N} \left(\frac{x}{n}\right)^k$$

$$= \sum_{j=0}^{n-1} \frac{x^j}{j!} + \frac{x^n}{n!} \frac{(1-u^{N+1})}{1(-u)} \tag{7.3}$$

where $u = \dfrac{x}{n}$

There is now no restriction on x/n for the convergence of the series since it is a finite series. If the queues build up in this case customers are turned away and this acts as a regulator on the queue size. A customer is turned away if on arrival there are $N+n$ customers in the system already. The chance of being turned away is hence $P(N+n)$.

Chance of a customer being turned away $= P(N+n)$

$$= \frac{x^n}{n!} u^N \cdot P(0) \tag{7.4}$$

The average waiting time of customers is

$$= \frac{1}{n\mu} \sum_{j=n}^{N+n-1} (j-n+1)\, P(j) = \frac{1}{n\mu} \frac{x^n}{n!} \sum_{i=0}^{N-1} (i+1)\, u^i P(0)$$

$$= \frac{1}{n\mu} \frac{x^n}{n!} \left\{ \frac{(1-u^N)}{(1-u)^2} - \frac{Nu^N}{(1-u)} \right\} P(0) \tag{7.5}$$

This formula 7.5 gives the average waiting time averaged over all customers. If the average waiting time for only those customers who are not turned away is required then this formula is divided by $(1-P)$ where P is the proportion of customers turned away given by equation 7.4.

Average waiting time of customers who obtain service

$$= \frac{1}{n\mu} \frac{x^n}{n!} \left\{ \frac{(1-u^N)}{(1-u)^2} - \frac{Nu^N}{(1-u)} \right\} \frac{P(0)}{[1-P(N+n)]} .$$

When $P(N+n)$ is small the value of average waiting time (7.5) becomes approximately equal to the value of average waiting time in the queue $M/M/n$ with no limit on the queue size. The values of the limit on queue size, N, for which there is no difference between these average waiting times to four decimal places are given in Table 7.1.

Table 7.1. TABLES OF THE MINIMUM LIMIT ON QUEUE SIZE, N, FOR WHICH THE RESULTS ON THE INFINITE QUEUE $M/M/n$ CAN BE APPLIED TO THE FINITE QUEUE TO THE ACCURACY OF 10^{-4}

Utilisation	Number of Servers n								
	2	3	4	5	6	7	8	9	10
0·1	3	3	2	1	1	1	1	1	1
0·2	4	3	3	2	2	2	1	1	1
0·3	8	7	6	6	6	5	3	2	2
0·4	12	10	10	9	8	7	7	7	7
0·5	15	15	15	12	12	12	12	10	10
0·6	22	21	21	21	19	17	16	16	16
0·7	32	31	31	31	29	29	26	26	26
0·8	51	49	49	49	47	47	47	47	47
0·9	108	107	107	106	106	106	104	104	104

It is necessary to calculate results for only these limits on queue size which are less than the values in the table since for limits above these values the results for the infinite queue are applicable. Tables of waiting time (Table A. 11) and chance of being turned away (Table A. 12) are given for only the values of queue limit below the critical values given above.

Example 7.1

A queueing system has limited space available, service points take up three times as much space as customers. Arrivals and service times both have negative exponential distributions. How many servers should be used if the proportion of customers turned away is to be as small as possible when the arrival rate is 4.5 customers per service time and there is sufficient space in total for 31 customers?

Since the servers occupy the space equivalent to three customers the alternatives are as shown in Table 7.2. From the tables of the chance a customer is turned away, interpolating linearly on the logarithm of the

Table 7.2.

Servers	5	6	7	8	9	10
Queue limit	16	13	10	7	4	1

Table 7.3.

System		Utilisation (u)	Chance of being turned away (P)
Servers (n)	Limit (N)		
5	16	0·9	0·0162
6	13	0·75	0·0024
7	10	0·64	0·0008
8	7	0·56	0·0007
9	4	0·50	0·0014
10	1	0·45	0·0044

probability for values of queue limit and also for values of utilisation the figures obtained are as shown in Table 7.3. The system with the smallest chance of a customer being turned away is that with 8 servers and space for 7 customers to wait if the servers are all occupied.

The average waiting time of customers (interpolating linearly for values of limit (N), and logarithmically for values of utilisation) is from the table 0·0266 of a service time.

If the service points had taken up only the space equivalent to a single customer then the policy to minimise the chance of the customer being turned away is obviously to use all the space available for servers. This special case is treated separately in a later section because it covers a wide range of applications.

Example 7.2

A petrol station has room for seven cars, including the ones at the pumps. The installation of a pump costs £15. per week, and the average profit on a customer is 1·25 p. The arrivals and service time both have negative exponential distributions. The arrival rate is 4 cars per service time. How many pumps should be installed for continuous running of a self service system? The service time is 1 min on average.

Using the tables of chance of being turned away and formula 7.4 where necessary the results obtained are as shown in Table 7.4. The number of pumps which will maximise the net profit is 5 with two spaces for customers to queue if all pumps are occupied, 9·9% of customers will be turned away in this case and the average waiting time of other customers is $0·080\,5 \times 1 = 0·080\,5$ min.

Table 7.4.

Number of Pumps (n)	Limit on Queue (N)	Utilisation (u)	Chance of being turned away (P)	Cost (£)	Profit (£)	Nett (£)
4	3	1·0	0·163 3	60	422	362
5	2	0·8	0·099 0	75	454	379
6	1	0·66	0·071 3	90	468	378

7.2.2 The Queue $D/M/n$ with a Limit of N Customers in the Queue

The probabilities of the number of customers in the system can be written down in the same way as the similar queue with no limit on queue size. It is more convenient in this case however to consider the system immediately before a customer arrives.

$P_t(j) = $ the chance there are j customers in the system at time t which is immediately before a customer arrives.

$$j = 0, 1, 2, \ldots, N+n$$

considering the probabilities an arrival interval later in time

$$P_{t+a}(0) = \sum_{j=0}^{N+n-1} P_t(j)\, d_{j+1}(j+1) + P_t(N+n)\, d_{N+n}(N+n)$$

$$P_{t+a}(1) = \sum_{j=0}^{N+n-1} P_t(j)\, d_{j+1}(j) + P_t(N+n)\, d_{N+n}(N+n-1)$$

$$P_{t+a}(k) = \sum_{j=k-1}^{N+n-1} P_t(j)\, d_{j+1}(j+1-k) + P_t(N+n)\, d_{N+n}(N+n-k)$$

$$\tag{7.6}$$

$$k = 1, 2, \ldots, N+n-1$$

Also
$$\sum_{j=0}^{N+n} P_t(j) = 1 \tag{7.7}$$

where $d_j(i)$ are as defined in equations 4.3–4.5.

The steady state equations come directly from these by suppressing the time parameter t, and can be solved numerically for any particular arrival rate and service time.

The chance a customer is turned away is $P(N+n)$

The chance a customer does not have to wait is $\sum_{j=0}^{n-1} P(j)$

The average waiting time of customers is

$$W = \frac{s}{n} \sum_{j=0}^{N-1} (j+1)P(n+j), \quad \text{where} \quad s = \text{average service time.}$$

7.2.3 The Queue $M/D/n$ with a Limit on the Customers in the Queue

The approach used to determine probabilities for the queue $M/D/n$ with no limit on queue size cannot be adapted to this case. In this queue with no limit the arrivals in a service time have a Poisson distribution, while in this case some of the arrivals could be turned away which modifies the arrival distribution. No results on this model are known to the author. It is possible to give the values of N above which the results for the queue $M/D/n$ with no limit on the queue can be applied. By calculating the steady state probabilities for $M/D/n$ the value of j for which $P(j)$ becomes less than the required accuracy of the results

Table 7.5. VALUES OF N FOR ABOVE WHICH THE STEADY STATE PROBABILITIES CAN BE ASSUMED

Utilisation (u)	Number of Servers (n)								
	2	3	4	5	6	7	8	9	10
0·10	3	2	2	1	1	1	1	1	1
0·20	4	4	4	4	3	3	2	2	2
0·30	6	5	5	5	5	5	5	4	4
0·40	7	7	7	7	7	7	7	7	6
0·50	10	9	9	9	9	9	9	9	9
0·60	13	13	13	13	12	12	12	12	12
0·70	18	18	18	18	18	17	17	17	17
0·80	27	27	27	27	27	27	27	27	27

can be found. If the value of $n+N$ is greater than the value of j the results for the infinite queue can be applied to the finite queue. If the value of $n+N$ is less than the value of j the results for the infinite queue may no longer be applicable.

The values of j for which the values of the probabilities are equal to the steady state probabilities to five decimal places are given in Table 7.5.

7.3 QUEUEING SYSTEMS IN WHICH NO WAITING IS ALLOWED

Much of the early work on queues by A. K. Erlang and C. Palm was applied to telephone systems. Automatic telephone exchanges are generally designed so that calls incoming when all lines are engaged cannot be held until a line becomes free and are hence lost. The proportion of lost calls must be kept below acceptable levels. Such a service system is a special case of the queueing system with limited waiting room, there being no waiting room at all. The proportion of lost calls in the telephone exchange will be the proportion of customers turned away in the queueing system.

A similar case where no queueing is allowed is that of a car park. Each parking space can be thought of as a service point. If all service points are full then all arrivals are turned away and must find a parking space elsewhere.

7.3.1 The Queue $M/M/n$ with no Waiting

A service system with n servers, random arrivals and negative exponential service times has the following steady state equations.

$$\lambda P(0) = \mu P(1)$$
$$(\lambda+j\mu) P(j) = (j+1) \mu P(j+1)+\lambda P(j-1) \qquad (7.8)$$
$$1 \leqslant j \leqslant n-1$$
$$n\mu P(n) = \lambda P(n-1)$$

where λ = the arrival rate of customers.
μ = the service rate.

n = the number of servers, and also the maximum number of customers in the system.

$P(j)$ = the chance of there being j customers in the system at any time in the steady state.

These have the solution

$$\left. \begin{array}{c} P(j) = \dfrac{x^j}{j!}\, P(0) \\[2mm] P(0)^{-1} = \displaystyle\sum_{j=0}^{n} \dfrac{x^j}{j!} \\[2mm] x = \lambda/\mu \end{array} \right\} \qquad (7.9)$$

The chance a customer is turned away from the system $= P(n)$

$$= \frac{x^n P(0)}{n!}$$

For n small $P(0)$ is easily calculated. For n large and x small $P(0)$ is approximately e^{-x} and $P(n)$ is the $(n+1)$th term of a Poisson distribution with mean x. The case which is most difficult to calculate is that where n is large and x is sufficiently large for the assumption $\sum_{j=0}^{n} \dfrac{x^j}{j!} \approx e^x$ not to hold.

In these conditions $P(n)$ can be written as

$$P(n) = \frac{x^n}{n!}\, P(0) = \frac{x^n}{n!} \bigg/ \sum_{j=0}^{n} \frac{x^j}{j!}$$

$$= \frac{x^n}{n!}\, e^{-x} \bigg/ \sum_{j=0}^{n} \frac{x^j}{j!}\, e^{-x} \qquad (7.10)$$

the denominator is the sum of the first $n+1$ terms of a Poisson distribution. For x reasonably large, as in the present case, the Poisson distribution can be approximated by the normal distribution with the same mean and standard deviation.

For x reasonably large (> 15)

$$P(n) \approx \frac{x^n}{n!}\, e^{-x} \bigg/ F(u) \qquad (7.11)$$

where

$$F(u) = \int_{-\infty}^{u} \frac{1}{(2\pi)^{1/2}} e^{-(1/2)x^2} \, dx, \text{ the standardised normal integral}$$

and

$$u = (n + \tfrac{1}{2} - x)/x^{1/2}$$

Example 7.3

Cars arrive at a car park in a Poisson stream at a rate of ten a minute. The length of time cars stay in the park has a negative exponential distribution with an average of three minutes. How large should the car park be if there is to be a 1% chance of a car being turned away because the park is full?

$$x = \lambda/\mu = 30 \qquad P(n) = 0.01 = \frac{x^n}{n!} e^{-x} \sum_{j=0}^{n} \frac{x^j}{j!} e^{-x}$$

using the normal approximation of equation 7.11

$$P(n) = 0.01 = \frac{x^n}{n!} e^{-x} \Big/ F(u) \quad \text{where} \quad u = \left(n + \frac{1}{2} - x\right) \Big/ x^{1/2}$$

$$P(n) = 0.01 = \{F(u) - F((n - x - \tfrac{1}{2})/x^{1/2})\}/F(u)$$

Taking n as the 99% point of a Poisson distribution with mean 30, $n = 42.76$, the right hand side of equation is 0.0048, which is too small. n must be decreased, so trying $n = 40$ the right hand side is 0.01419. Interpolating, $n = 40.84$ and the right hand side now becomes 0.01052.

The car park should have capacity for 41 cars. If an exact calculation of the probabilities $P(n)$ is performed the results are as shown in Table 7.6.

Table 7.6.

n	40	41	42	43
$P(n)$	0.01444	0.01044	0.00744	0.00551

The exact calculations are most easily performed by obtaining the probabilities in terms of the highest in value. Since equations 7.8 reduce to

$$P(j) = \frac{x}{j} P(j-1) \qquad j \geqslant 1$$

$P(j)$ will be bigger than $P(j-1)$ if $x > j$ and less than $P(j-1)$ if $j > x$.

Table 7.7.

j	$(j+1)/x = a_j$	$b_{j+1}a_j = b_j$	j	a_j	b_j
30	—	1·000 0	19	20/30	0·123 1
29	1·0	1·000 0	18	19/30	0·078 0
28	29/30	0·966 7	17	18/30	0·046 8
27	28/30	0·902 2	16	17/30	0·026 5
26	27/30	0·812 0	15	16/30	0·014 1
25	26/30	0·703 7	14	15/30	0·007 1
24	25/30	0·586 4	13	14/30	0·003 3
23	24/30	0·469 2	12	13/30	0·001 4
22	23/30	0·359 7	11	12/30	0·000 6
21	22/30	0·263 8	10	11/30	0·000 2
20	21/30	0·184 7	9	10/30	0·000 1
					$\Sigma b_j = 7\cdot549\,4$

Table 7.8.

N	$a_N = x/N$	$b_N = b_{N-1}a_N$	$P(N) = b_N \big/ \sum_{j=0}^{N} b_j$
31	30/31	0·967 7	0·113 6
32	30/32	0·907 3	0·096 3
33	30/33	0·824 8	0·080 5
34	30/34	0·727 7	0·066 3
35	30/35	0·623 8	0·053 8
36	30/36	0·519 8	0·042 9
37	30/37	0·421 5	0·033 6
38	30/38	0·332 7	0·025 8
39	30/39	0·256 0	0·019 5
40	30/40	0·192 0	0·014 4
41	30/41	0·140 5	0·010 4
42	30/42	0·100 3	0·007 4
43	30/43	0·070 0	0·005 1

The modal probabiilty will hence be at $j =$ the integer below $x\ (= m$ say). For $j < m$ the equation can be written in the form

$$P(j) = \frac{(j+1)}{x} P(j+1) = b_j P(m)$$

and for $j > m$, $P(j) = \frac{x}{j} P(j-1) = b_j P(m)$

In this example $x = 30$, so $m = 30$ (see Table 7.7) For $N > 30$ see Table 7.8.

Utilisation of the System

The average number of servers working is $\sum\limits_{j=0}^{n} jP(j)$

$$= x \sum\limits_{0}^{n-1} \frac{x^j}{j!} P(0) = x[1 - P(n)]$$

utilisation $= U = x[1 - P(n)]/n = \dfrac{x}{n} [1 - P(n)]$

$\qquad =$ utilisation if no customers are turned away $\times$ proportion not turned away.

Average Busy Period of the System

This can be found by identical argument to that given for the queue $M/M/n$ to be $\bar{B}$ where

$$\bar{B} = (1 - P(0))/(\lambda P(0)) \tag{7.12}$$

Average Busy Period of Individual Servers

If a server on finishing the service of a customer finds there are no more customers waiting for service, the server will be idle until one or more customers have arrived. The duration of the idle period for the server will depend on the arrival rate of customers, and the rules governing the order in which servers return to service if there are more than one available to serve a customer on his arrival. If the servers return to service in the order they came out of service then the average idle time of individual servers can be found. With this server discipline a server finding j servers idle on finishing service, including the server just finished service, will recommence serving when the jth next customer arrives. Since the arrivals have a negative exponential distribution and none will be turned away in this situation the average length of the idle period will be j/λ. The steady state probabilities apply for any point in time and hence for a point at which a server becomes idle so

$a(j)$ = probability a server finds j servers idle on completing service

$\quad = P(n-j)/[1-P(n)]$

Average idle period of individual servers $= \sum\limits_{j=1}^{n} \dfrac{j}{\lambda} a(j)$

$$= \sum\limits_{j=1}^{n} jP(n-j)/\{\lambda[1-P(n)]\}$$

$$= n/\{\lambda[1-P(n)]\}-x/\lambda = I \qquad (7.13)$$

Since idle and busy periods alternate for individual servers and the utilisation of the system is U, the number of idle periods is equal to the number of busy periods over a long period of time, T say, hence,

number of idle periods $= \dfrac{T(1-U)}{I}$ = number of busy periods $= \dfrac{TU}{B}$

where B is the average busy period for an individual server.

$$B = \frac{IU}{(1-U)} = x/\lambda \qquad (7.14)$$

Duration of Periods when Customers are turned away

Customers are turned away from the system when all n servers are busy. The length of time such periods of full utilisation will last will have a negative exponential distribution with an average of $1/n\mu$. The individual service times have a negative exponential distribution each with average $1/\mu$, when n servers having the distribution of service are working at the same time, the interval between successive customers departing from the system will have a negative exponential distribution with an average of $1/n\mu$. The time the present system will be fully occupied will be one such interval and hence has a negative exponential distribution with an average of $1/n\mu$. The distribution of the time between a customer being turned away and the system coming to the end of a fully occupied period will be the remainder of such an interval which has of course still a negative exponential distribution with the average of $1/n\mu$.

If t is the duration of a period when the system is fully occupied, and $f(t)$ is its probability density function, then

$$f(t) = n\mu e^{-n\mu t} \qquad (7.15)$$

The duration T_p at which a proportion p of these periods are on average shorter in duration is given by

$$p = \int_0^{T_p} f(t)\,\mathrm{d}t = 1 - e^{-n\mu T_p}$$

$$e^{-n\mu T_p} = 1 - p$$

taking logs

$$-n\mu T_p = \log_e (1-p)$$

$$T_p = -\log_e (1-p)/n\mu \qquad (7.16)$$

since $1/n\mu$ is the average duration of the interval.

$$T_p/\text{average duration} = -\log_e (1-p)$$

which can easily be found for a range of values for p (see Table 7.9).

Table 7.9.

p	0·50	0·90	0·95	0·99	0·999
T_p/average duration	0·69	2·30	3·00	4·61	6·91

So half the periods will be over before 0·69×average duration and 95% of the periods over before 3×average duration.

7.3.2 The Queue $M/E_k/n$ with no Waiting

If a system similar to the previous is considered with a constant service time instead of a negative exponential distribution the steady state equations are difficult to obtain. Consideration of the case with the more general Erlang distribution is easier, since it can be thought of as being built up of several 'phases' each of which has a negative exponential distribution. The service rate can still be denoted by μ, so the rate at which customers pass through each of the k 'phases' of service will be $k\mu$. The service time distribution $f(t)$ is now of the form

$$f(t) = (k\mu)^k t^{k-1} e^{-k\mu t}/k! \qquad (7.17)$$

Let the arrival rate be still denoted by λ. The system can now be described completely if account is taken of the number of 'phases' of the service time each customer has to go through at any time.

Let $P(j, n_1, n_2, \ldots, n_k) =$ the probability there are j customers in the system at any time, of which n_1 will have one 'phase' of service to complete before departure, n_2 will have two 'phases', etc., up to n_k with k 'phases' to complete. There being a restriction on the sum of the values of n_i namely,

$$\sum_{i=1}^{k} n_i = j \qquad (7.18)$$

The steady state probability equations are

$$(\lambda + jk\mu) P(j; n_1, n_2, \ldots, n_k) = \lambda P(j-1; n_1, n_2, \ldots, n_k-1)$$
$$+ \sum_{i=2}^{k} (n_i+1) k\mu P(j; n_1, n_2, \ldots, n_{i-1}-1, n_i+1, \ldots, n_k)$$
$$+ (n_1+1) k\mu P(j+1; n_1+1, n_2, \ldots, n_k)$$
$$0 \leqslant j \leqslant n \qquad n_i \geqslant 0$$

provided $P(j; n_1, n_2, \ldots, n_k)$ for negative values of any of j, n_1, n_2, $\ldots$, n_k are taken as zero; and also when $j > n$.
The general solution to these equations is

$$P(j; n_1, n_2, \ldots, n_k) = \frac{Ay^j}{n_1! \, n_2!, \ldots, n_k!}$$

where $y = (\lambda/k\mu)$

summing over all allowable values of the n_is for a fixed value of j will give the probability there are j customers in the system.

$$P(j) = \sum_{n_i} P(j; n_1, n_2, \ldots, n_k) = \sum_{n_i} \frac{Ay^j}{n_1! \, n_2! \ldots n_k!}$$

$$= A \frac{y^j k^j}{j!}$$

$$= \frac{A}{j!} \left(\frac{\lambda}{\mu}\right)^j = A \frac{x^j}{j!} \tag{7.19}$$

where $x = \lambda/\mu$ = average number of arrivals in a service time

since the probabilities sum to unity

$$1 = \sum_{j=0}^{n} A \frac{x^j}{j!}, \qquad A^{-1} = \sum_{j=0}^{n} \frac{x^j}{j!} \tag{7.20}$$

The probabilities $P(j)$ are identical with those for the case previously considered, given in equation 7.9. Any results on the $M/M/n$ case using the values of $P(j)$ can now be applied directly to this case. The average idle period will be given by equation 7.13 and the average busy period by equation 7.14.

7.4 Problems

1. A garage takes 60 s exactly to deal with one car. Cars requiring petrol pass the garage on average every 30 s in a Poisson stream. There is room for two cars at the garage, including the one being served. What is the chance of being turned away because there is no room to pull into the garage? If the space was enlarged to take 3 cars, what would be the proportion of cars which would now obtain service?

2. The management of a supermarket are providing a car park for their customers to use. It is intended that only one customer in a hundred on average will be turned away because the park is full. The length of time a customer leaves his car in the park has a negative exponential distribution with an average of three minutes, this distribution being unaltered by the number of customers in the supermarket. Customers in cars are expected to arrive at the rate of ten a minute with a negative

exponential distribution of interval between arrivals. What should the capacity of the park be?

3. A telephone exchange has calls for trunk lines at a rate of one a minute with a negative exponential distribution of intervals between such calls. The duration of a trunk call has a negative exponential distribution with an average of three minutes. Calls for trunk lines cannot be held if all the lines are engaged and are 'lost'. What is the smallest number of trunk lines required at the exchange if no more than one in a hundred calls on average are to be lost?

4. The distribution of service time at a petrol station has an Erlang distribution with an average of 60 s. The are are four service points at the station and no room for cars to wait if all service points are engaged. Cars requiring petrol pass the station in a Poisson stream at a rate of one every 30 s. What proportion of cars will be unable to obtain service? How many service points are required if the proportion of cars turned away is to be less than one in two hundred on average?

CHAPTER 8

Queues with Arrivals Dependent on Queue Size

All the queues studied in previous chapters have had the arrival rates the same whatever the state of the queue. In some practical queueing situations it is felt the arrival rates depend on the queue size, customers being discouraged from joining the queue when it is large because of the time they would have to wait to get served. This is true of situations where the customer has alternative ways of obtaining the service required, as in shopping, purchase of raw materials, etc. The chance of a customer not joining the queue should intuitively increase as the queue gets larger, so models in which the 'balking' increases with the queue size will be considered first.

8.1 $M/M/1$ WITH BALKING

The simple single server queue with random arrivals and negative exponential service times is considered again with the modification that a customer arriving to find n customers already in the system joins the queue with probability α^n where α is a constant between 0 and 1. The probability of joining the queue decays exponentially with the size of queue at a greater or lesser rate dependent on the value of α.

Let λ = arrival rate of customers before balking
μ = service rate

the steady state probabilities are given by:

$$\lambda P(0) = \mu P(1)$$
$$(\mu + \lambda \alpha^n) P(n) = \mu P(n+1) + \lambda \alpha^{n-1} P(n-1)$$
$$1 \leqslant n < \infty \tag{8.1}$$

giving the solution $P(n) = \dfrac{\lambda}{\mu} \alpha^{n-1} P(n-1)$

if $u = \lambda/\mu$ this can be reduced to

$$P(n) = u^n \alpha^{(n/2)(n-1)} P(0) \tag{8.2}$$
$$0 \leqslant n < \infty$$

and summing the probabilities to unity

$$P(0)^{-1} = \sum_{n=0}^{\infty} u^n \alpha^{(n/2)(n-1)} \tag{8.3}$$
$$0 \leqslant n < \infty$$

The utilisation of the system $= 1 - P(0)$
the utilisation of the system without balking is u, so the proportion of customers not deterred by the queue size from joining the queue is $[1 - P(0)]/u$, which gives the proportion of customers who 'balk'

$$= 1 - [1 - P(0)]/u \tag{8.4}$$

Average number of customers in the queue $= \sum_{n=1}^{\infty} (n-1) P(n)$

$$= \sum_{n=0}^{\infty} n P(n) - [1 - P(0)]$$

$$= \text{average number of customers in the system}$$
$$- [1 - P(0)] \tag{8.5}$$

Average number of customers in the system $= \sum_{n=0}^{\infty} n P(n)$

The distribution of waiting time $f(t)$ is

$$f(t) = \sum_{n=1}^{\infty} \frac{\mu^n t^{n-1} e^{-\mu t}}{(n-1)!} \alpha^n P(n) \tag{8.6}$$

Table 8.1. CHANCE THE SERVER IS IDLE, $P(0)$ IN THE QUEUE $M/M/1$ WITH BALKING

| α | \multicolumn{10}{c}{u = Utilisation of Server prior to Balking} |
	0·1	0·2	0·3	0·4	0·5	0·6	0·7	0·8	0·9	1·0
0·1	0·9083	0·8306	0·7639	0·7062	0·6557	0·6112	0·5716	0·5363	0·5046	0·4700
0·2	0·9074	0·8278	0·7586	0·6891	0·6447	0·5975	0·5553	0·5176	0·4836	0·4529
0·3	0·9066	0·8249	0·7532	0·6898	0·6335	0·5835	0·5387	0·4985	0·4623	0·4296
0·4	0·9057	0·8220	0·7475	0·6811	0·6218	0·5687	0·5211	0·4784	0·4399	0·4052
0·5	0·9049	0·8190	0·7416	0·6719	0·6092	0·5528	0·5021	0·4565	0·4155	0·3786
0·6	0·9040	0·8158	0·7352	0·6618	0·5952	0·5350	0·4807	0·4318	0·3879	0·3485
0·7	0·9031	0·8124	0·7282	0·6505	0·5793	0·5145	0·4557	0·4028	0·3554	0·3131
0·8	0·9021	0·8087	0·7203	0·6375	0·5604	0·4895	0·4249	0·3665	0·3144	0·2682
0·9	0·9011	0·8046	0·7112	0·6215	0·5363	0·4564	0·3824	0·3153	0·2556	0·2036
1·0	0·9000	0·8000	0·7000	0·6000	0·5000	0·4000	0·3000	0·2000	0·1000	0·0000

Table 8.2. AVERAGE NUMBER OF CUSTOMERS IN SYSTEM, $\sum_0^\infty nP(n)$

α	$u = $ Utilisation of System prior to Balking									
	0·1	0·2	0·3	0·4	0·5	0·6	0·7	0·8	0·9	1·0
0·1	0·0926	0·1728	0·2430	0·3052	0·3609	0·4111	0·4568	0·4985	0·5370	0·5726
0·2	0·0944	0·1790	0·2554	0·3250	0·3888	0·4476	0·5022	0·5530	0·6005	0·6450
0·3	0·0962	0·1853	0·2683	0·3458	0·4183	0·4865	0·5508	0·6115	0·6689	0·7234
0·4	0·0980	0·1920	0·2821	0·3683	0·4508	0·5298	0·6055	0·6779	0·7474	0·8139
0·5	0·0999	0·1991	0·2971	0·3935	0·4879	0·5801	0·6700	0·7574	0·8423	0·9246
0·6	0·1018	0·2068	0·3140	0·4226	0·5319	0·6413	0·7501	0·8580	0·9645	1·0692
0·7	0·1039	0·2153	0·3335	0·4576	0·5868	0·7201	0·8565	0·9951	1·1350	1·2753
0·8	0·1061	0·2249	0·3569	0·5021	0·6603	0·8309	1·0129	1·2051	1·4059	1·6136
0·9	0·1085	0·2362	0·3866	0·5637	0·7713	1·0132	1·2925	1·6110	1·9690	2·3646
1·0	0·1111	0·2500	0·4286	0·6667	1·0000	1·5000	2·3333	4·0000	9·0000	∞

and the average waiting time

$$= \sum_{n=1}^{\infty} \frac{n}{\mu} \alpha^n P(n) = \frac{1}{\lambda} \sum_{0}^{\infty} n P(n+1) \qquad (8.7)$$

The average busy period of the server can be found by the usual argument for a single server queue with random arrivals.

Average busy period of server $= [1 - P(0)]/\lambda P(0)$ (8.8)

While it is unlikely that the series for $P(0)$ in equation 8.3 can be summed algebraically it can be evaluated numerically. Since all the factors calculated can be reduced to functions of either $P(0)$ or $\sum nP(n)$ these two functions are tabulated for a range of values of u and α (see Tables 8.1 and 8.2).

The model reduces to the queue $M/M/1$ without balking when $\alpha = 1$, which is tabulated for comparison. Linear interpolation in the tables gives reasonable accuracy but the probabilities for any value of u and α can be found easily from equation 8.2 and hence the value of the average number of customers in the system. All other factors can be found in terms of these two values.

From the recurrence relation $P(j) = u\alpha^{j-1}P(j-1)$ for the probabilities it is obvious that eventually for any α less than unity $P(j)$ will be less than $P(j-1)$ and that steady state solutions will exist for any value of u and $\alpha < 1$. A system of this type which is potentially overloaded $(u > 1)$ will stabilise owing to the balking of customers when long queues build up.

Example 8.1

A single server system with random arrivals and exponential service time has customers joining the system with probability α^j when there are j customers already in the system where $\alpha = 0.9$. What value of average service time is required in the system if only 1% of customers balk from joining the queue on average? The average arrival rate is 2 customers per minute.

From equation 8.4 the proportion of customers who balk from joining the queue is $1 - [1 - P(0)]/u$ for $\alpha = 0.9$, from the table for $P(0)$ is obtained:

u	0·1	0·2
proportion balking	0·011	0·023

so u should be below 0·1 and should satisfy the equation

$$1 - [1 - P(0)]/u = 0·01 \quad \text{where} \quad P(0)^{-1} = \sum_{0}^{\infty} u^{n} \alpha^{(1/2)n(n-1)}$$

using Newton's method to solve this equation starting with an initial estimate of $u = 0·1$ the value of u satisfying the equation is found to be 0·0935, since $u = \lambda/\mu$ and $\lambda = 2$ customers per minute, the service rate $\mu = \lambda/u = 2/0·0935$, and hence the average service time, $1/\mu$ is $0·0935/2 = 0·0468$ min.

8.2. $M/M/1$ WITH AN ALTERNATIVE FORM OF BALKING

The model above had customers balk from joining the queue with probabilities which were dependent on the queue size and in the form of a geometric series. An alternative form is to have the probability of joining be inversely proportional to the number of customers in the queue; i.e. a customer arriving to find j customers in the system has a chance $1/(j+1)$ of joining the queue and a chance $j/(j+1)$ of balking. In the special case of a customer finding the system empty the chance of joining is unity, i.e. the customers do not balk when the server is free to serve them.

The steady state equations now become

$$\lambda P(0) = \mu P(1)$$
$$(\mu + \lambda/(n+1)) P(n) = \mu P(n+1) + \frac{\lambda}{n} P(n-1) \tag{8.9}$$
$$1 \leqslant n < \infty$$

where $\lambda =$ arrival rate before balking, $\mu =$ service rate, these reduce to the recurrence relationship

$$P(n) = \frac{\lambda}{n\mu} P(n-1)$$
$$1 \leqslant n < \infty$$
$$= \frac{x^n}{n!} P(0) \tag{8.10}$$

where $x = \lambda/\mu$

summing

$$\sum_0^\infty P(n) = 1 = P(0) \sum_0^\infty x^n/n! = P(0)\, e^x$$

$$P(0) = e^{-x}$$

$$\therefore \quad P(n) = \frac{x^n}{n!}\, e^{-x} \tag{8.11}$$

$$0 \leqslant n < \infty$$

The steady state probabilities reduce to the Poisson distribution with an average of x. No condition on x is necessary for the steady state other than the usual conditions on the average of the Poisson distribution that it must be non-negative and finite. Values of x greater than unity imply the system would be overloaded if there was no balking of the customers and no steady state would be possible. The balking can thought of as a means of controlling the queue size, and is a sufficient control no matter how overloaded the system is. The usual factors of interest can now be calculated for the system.

The utilisation of the system $= 1 - P(0) = 1 - e^{-x}$. The arrival rate of the customers per service time before balking is $\lambda/\mu (= x)$ and without balking is the utilisation of the system, so the proportion of customers who do not balk is $[1 - P(0)]/x$, and hence

The proportion of customers who balk at joining the queue

$$= 1 - (1 - e^{-x})/x \tag{8.12}$$

Average number of customers in the queue

$$= \sum_1^\infty (n-1)\, P(n)$$

$$= x - 1 + e^{-x} \tag{8.13}$$

Average number of customers in the system

$$= \Sigma\, nP(n) = x$$

The distribution of waiting time is $f(t)$ where

$$f(t) = \sum_1^\infty \frac{\mu^n t^{n-1} \mathrm{e}^{-\mu t}}{(n-1)!} \frac{P(n)}{(n+1)} = \sum_1^\infty \frac{\mu^n t^{n-1} \mathrm{e}^{-\mu t}}{(n-1)!\,(n+1)!} x^n \mathrm{e}^{-x}$$

$$= \mu x\, \mathrm{e}^{-(\mu t + x)} \sum_{j=0}^\infty \frac{(\mu t x)^j}{j!\,(j+2)!}$$

$$= \frac{1}{t}\, \mathrm{e}^{-(\mu t + x)} \sum_{j=0}^\infty \frac{(-1)^{2j} y^{2j+2}}{2^{2j+2}\, j!\,(j+2)!}$$

where $y = 2(\mu t x)^{1/2}$

$$f(t) = \frac{1}{t}\, \mathrm{e}^{-(\mu t + x)} I_2(y) \tag{8.14}$$

where $I_2(y)$ is the modified Bessel function of the first kind.

Since the arrival interval distribution is negative exponential when the server is idle the average busy period of the server is

$$\frac{[1 - P(0)]}{\lambda P(0)} = (\mathrm{e}^x - 1)/\lambda \tag{8.15}$$

Making comparisons between the two models it is possible to calculate the values of α which, for the same value of x, gives the same proportion of customers balking in each model. The equation for α in this case is obtained when the proportion in equation 8.12 is the same as the proportion given by equation 8.4, that is when

$$1 - [1 - P(0)]/x = 1 - (1 - \mathrm{e}^{-x})/x$$

or
$$P(0) = \mathrm{e}^{-x}$$

where $P(0)^{-1} = \displaystyle\sum_{n=0}^\infty x^n \alpha^{(n/2)(n-1)}$

giving
$$\mathrm{e}^x = \sum_{n=0}^\infty x^n \alpha^{(n/2)(n-1)} \tag{8.16}$$

This equation can be solved numerically and the average number in the queue calculated for each model for any value of x. If values of x less than unity are considered, i.e. systems which would not be overloaded even without balking the results for $x = 0 \cdot 1$, $(0 \cdot 1)$, $0 \cdot 9$ are given in Table 8.3.

Table 8.3. COMPARISON OF BALKING MODELS

Arrival Rate prior to Balking per Service Time	*Value of α for Equal Balking (equation 8.16)*	*Proportion of Customers who Balk on either Model (equation 8.12)*	*Average Number of Customers in Queue*	
			Model 1 (equation 8.5)	*Model 2 (equation 8.13)*
x				
0·1	0·504 1	0·051 7	0·004 8	0·004 8
0·2	0·508 1	0·107 0	0·018 4	0·018 7
0·3	0·512 1	0·166 2	0·039 8	0·040 8
0·4	0·515 9	0·229 6	0·068 1	0·070 3
0·5	0·519 6	0·297 4	0·102 4	0·106 5
0·6	0·523 3	0·370 2	0·142 0	0·148 8
0·7	0·526 9	0·448 2	0·186 2	0·196 6
0·8	0·530 4	0·531 9	0.234 5	0·249 3
0·9	0·533 8	0·621 8	0·286 4	0·306 6

The value of α stays fairly constant at 0·5 indicating the predominance of the probabilities $P(n)$ for small values of n, i.e. $n = 0, 1, 2$, where the balking rates would be roughly equivalent on either model at this value of α. The average number of customers in the queue is always higher in the second model showing the probabilities $P(n)$ decrease more rapidly with n in the first model than in the second.

Example 8.2

If arrivals at a system described in the model above are at a rate of ten a minute prior to balking, and the average busy period of the server is to be not more than 5 min, what is the proportion of customers that will balk, if the service time is as large as the restriction allows?

λ = the arrival rate = ten per minute

The average busy period from equation 8.15 is $(e^x - 1)/\lambda$ where $x = \lambda/\mu$, μ = the service rate, so if the average busy period is to be less than 5 min,

$$(e^x - 1)/10 < 5$$

$e^x < 51$ or $x < \log_e 51 = 3{\cdot}93183$

i.e. $\dfrac{\lambda}{\mu} < 3{\cdot}931\,83,$ $\mu > 10/3{\cdot}931\,83,$

average service time $= \dfrac{1}{\mu} < 0{\cdot}393\,183$

the largest average service time allowable $= 0{\cdot}393\,183$ min. The proportion of customers who balk is $1 - (1 - e^{-x})/x$ which, for $x = 3{\cdot}931\,83$, is $1 - (1 - 1/51)/3{\cdot}931\,83$.

$= 0{\cdot}750\,65$

The utilisation of the server $= 1 - e^{-x} = 50/51 = 98{\cdot}04\%$.

8.3. MULTISERVER QUEUES WITH BALKING OF CUSTOMERS

8.3.1 $M/M/n$ with Balking

Both the models described above can be extended to cover multiserver systems, considering the models in turn:

$\lambda =$ arrival rate of customers prior to balking
$\mu =$ service rate of a server.

The distribution of arrivals and service time are both negative exponential in form. The chance a customer arriving to find k customers queueing will join the queue is α^k. Hence the chance such a customer will balk at joining the queue is $(1 - \alpha^k)$. If $P(j)$ is the steady state probability of there being j customers in the system, the equations for these probabilities are:

$$\lambda P(0) = \mu P(1)$$
$$(\lambda + j\mu)\,P(j) = (j+1)\,\mu P(j+1) + \lambda P(j-1)$$
$$1 \leqslant j < n$$
$$(\alpha^{j+1}\lambda + n\mu)\,P(j+n) = n\mu P(j+n+1) + \alpha^j \lambda P(j+n-1) \quad (8.17)$$
$$0 \leqslant j < \infty$$

The solutions reduce to

$$P(j) = \frac{1}{j!} \left(\frac{\lambda}{\mu}\right)^j P(0) \qquad 0 \leqslant j \leqslant n \qquad (8.18)$$

$$P(n+j) = \alpha^j u P(n+j-1)$$

$$= u^j \alpha^{(1/2j)(j+1)} P(n) = u^j \frac{\alpha^{(j/2)(j+1)}}{n!} \left(\frac{\lambda}{\mu}\right)^n P(0) \quad (8.19)$$

$$0 \leqslant j < \infty$$

where $u = \dfrac{\lambda}{n\mu}$

$$P(0)^{-1} = \sum_{j=0}^{n-1} m^j/j! + \sum_{j=0}^{\infty} u^j \alpha^{(j/2)(j+1)} m^n/n! \qquad (8.20)$$

where $m = \lambda/\mu$

No restriction on u is necessary since the series will converge for any value of $|\alpha|$ less than unity. While the series cannot be summed algebraically it can be found numerically for any chosen values of u and α. The utilisation of the system is:

$$\left[n - \sum_{j=0}^{n-1}(n-j)P(j)\right]\bigg/n = 1-(n-m)\sum_{0}^{n-2}P(j)/m - P(n-1)/n = U$$

$$(8.21)$$

The proportion of customers who balk at joining the queue

$$= 1 - nU/m = 1 - U/u \qquad (8.22)$$

The average number of customers in the system $= \sum_{0}^{\infty} jP(j)$

The average number of customers in the queue $= \sum_{j=n}^{\infty}(j-n)P(j)$

The average waiting time of customers $= \sum_{j=n}^{\infty} \frac{(j+1-n)}{n\mu}\alpha^{j+1-n}P(j)$

$$= \sum_{j=n}^{\infty}(j+1-n)P(j+1)/\lambda = \text{Average number of customers in queue}/\lambda.$$

$$(8.23)$$

If servers return to service after an idle period in the order in which they become idle then a server becoming idle when i servers are already idle will have an average idle period of $(i+1)$ arrival intervals. Since arrivals at such times will have a negative exponential inter arrival distribution,

$$\text{average idle interval} = \frac{\sum_0^{n-1} P(i)(i+1)}{\lambda \sum_0^{n-1} P(i)} = I \qquad (8.24)$$

Since the utilisation of the servers is known the proportion of time idle can be found. Since busy and idle periods alternate the number of each type will be equal in the long term so for a period of time T, the relationship between I and B the average busy period is:

$$T(1-U)/I = TU/B$$

$$B = \frac{IU}{(1-U)} \qquad (8.25)$$

Since the values of $P(i)$ for i less than n do not depend on α the value of I is obviously not a function of α as one would expect; B however does depend on α through the utilisation U.

It is possible to obtain the distribution of waiting time in terms of the probabilities $P(j)$ and since the series cannot be summed algebraically it is left in its elementary form. This can be evaluated numerically if required in any specific application.

Distribution function of waiting time $f(t)$

$$= \sum_{j=0}^{\infty} (\mu n)^{j+1} t^j \, e^{-\mu n t} \alpha^{j+1} P(n+j)/j!$$

If μ is then taken as 1, that is the times are measured in units of service time, and n is taken as the integer above $m = \lambda/\mu$. The system without balking will be working with the minimum number of servers required not to have the system overloaded. The effect of varying the balking rate α on the system can be calculated for a range of values of m.

The proportion of customers who balk is at its highest at about 38% (see Figure 8.1) when the arrival rate is just under two customers per service time and is decreased by the introduction of a further server when the arrival rate exceeds two. For values of α greater than 0·1 the

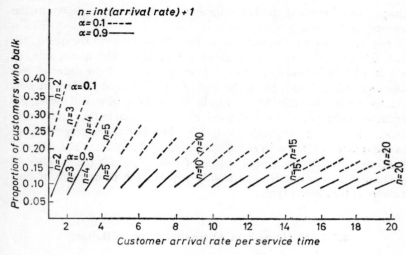

Fig. 8.1

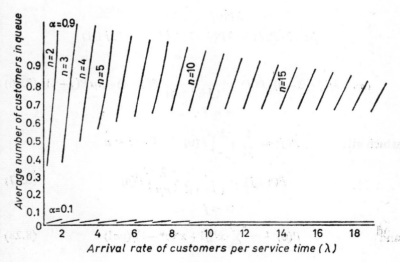

Fig. 8.2

graph has a similar shape but is smaller in magnitude, as shown by the curve for $\alpha = 0\cdot 9$.

Figure 8.2 shows the average number of customers in the queue, for $\alpha = 0\cdot 9$ and $0\cdot 1$, over the range of arrival rates. The queue size for $\alpha = 0\cdot 1$ is very small over the whole range and is of the order of one customer for $\alpha = 0\cdot 9$. Since the average waiting time of customers is related to the number in the queue the waiting time will never get excessive even though high utilisations are obtained in the cases evaluated. The average number in the queue is less than the average number in the queue $M/M/n$ with equal utilisation of the system. The effect of balking then even with high values of α is to reduce the number of customers in the queue significantly without the proportion of customers balked being large.

8.3.2 $M/M/n$ with an Alternative Form of Balking

If the form of balking considered in Section 8.2 is adapted to the multiserver queue, the chance a customer joins a queue of size j is taken as $1/(j+1)$ as in the previous section. The steady state equations are, with the usual notation;

$$\lambda P(0) = \mu P(1)$$

$$(j\mu + \lambda) P(j) = \lambda P(j-1) + (j+1)\mu P(j+1)$$

$$1 \leqslant j < n$$

$$(n\mu + \lambda/(j+2-n)) P(j) = \frac{\lambda}{(j+1-n)} P(j-1) + n\mu P(j+1) \quad (8.26)$$

$$n \leqslant j < \infty$$

which give

$$P(j) = \frac{1}{j!} \left(\frac{\lambda}{\mu}\right)^{j} P(0) \qquad 1 \leqslant j \leqslant n$$

$$P(n+j) = \frac{1}{(j+1)!} \left(\frac{\lambda}{n\mu}\right)^{j} P(n) \qquad (8.27)$$

$$0 \leqslant j < \infty$$

and

$$P(0)^{-1} = \sum_{j=0}^{n-1} x^{j}/j! + x^{n}(e^{u}-1)/(un!) \qquad (8.28)$$

$$u = x/n$$

The probabilities for $j < n$ are in proportion to probabilities in a Poisson distribution with average x, for $j > n$ the probabilities are in proportion to probabilities from a Poisson distribution with mean u, the correspondence being between $P(j+n)$ in the present system and $P(j+1)$ in the Poisson distribution.

The average number of customers in the system

$$= \sum_0^\infty jP(j) = xP(0) \sum_0^{n-2} x^j/j! + P(n)\,(e^u + (n-1)\,(e^u - 1)/u) \qquad (8.29)$$

Average number of customers in the queue

$$= \sum_0^\infty jP(n+j) = P(n)\,(e^u - (e^u - 1)/u) \qquad (8.30)$$

Utilisation of the system $=$

$$uP(0) \sum_0^{n-2} x^j/j! + P(n)\,(e^u - 1)/u = U \qquad (8.31)$$

The proportion of customers balked

$$= 1 - nU/x \qquad (8.32)$$

Distribution of waiting time of customers is $f(t)$ where

$$f(t) = \sum_0^\infty \frac{P(j+n)}{(j+2)}\,\frac{(n\mu)^{j+1}t^j}{j!}\,e^{-n\mu t}$$

$$= \frac{x^n}{n!}\,P(0)n\mu e^{-n\mu t} \sum_0^\infty (\lambda t)^j/[j!\,(j+2)!]$$

$$= \frac{x^n}{n!}\,P(0)\,\frac{n\mu}{\lambda t}\,e^{-n\mu t}I_2(y) \qquad (8.33)$$

where $y = 2(\lambda t)^{1/2}$ and $I_2(y)$ is the modified Bessel function of the first kind.

If servers return to service in the order in which they become idle the average busy period of individual servers can be found by arguments previously used. The probability a server becomes idle to find j servers already idle is $P(j)\Big/\sum_0^{n-1} P(j)$. Such a server will be idle until the $(j+1)$th customer arrives and hence the average idle time is $(j+1)/\lambda$.

The average idle time overall is $\bar{I}$ where,

$$\bar{I} = \sum_0^{n-1} (j+1)\, P(j)/\lambda \sum_0^{n-1} P(j) = \left[1 + x \sum_0^{n-2} P(j) \Big/ \sum_0^{n-1} P(j)\right]\Big/\lambda$$

Hence the average busy period, $\bar{B} = \bar{I}U/(1 - U)$ (8.34)

8.3.3 Comparison of Multiserver Balking Models

The two multiserver models considered can be compared in the same way as the single server models were compared. The multiserver model discussed in Section 8.3.1 is more general than the one discussed in Section 8.3.2 because it has an extra parameter α which gives flexibility to the rate of balking of customers. The value of α which gives the same proportion of customers balked on either model for identical arrival rates per service time (λ/μ) and the same number of servers can be found by equating the formulas 8.32 and 8.22. This reduces to the expression

$$\sum_0^\infty u^j/(j+1)! = \sum_0^\infty u^j \alpha^{(j/2)(j+1)} \qquad (8.35)$$

where $u = \lambda/n\mu$.

i.e. $(e^u - 1)/u = \sum_0^\infty u^j \alpha^{(j/2)(j+1)}$

this equation does not involve n explicitly only implicitly in u, the utilisation of the system prior to balking. The value of α can be found for a range of values of u. The range considered is from 0 to 1, i.e. the system is assumed always to have enough servers to deal with the arrival rate of customers prior to balking. The values of α obtained will be identical with those in Table 8.3. since the equation 8.35 does not depend on n but only on u which is equivalent to x in Table 8.3. The average number of customers in the system and in the queue in each of the models do of course depend on the number of servers in the system. If the number of servers in the system is taken as the integer above the average arrivals in a service time the system is specified once this arrival rate is known. The comparisons of the two models are summarised in the Table 8.4.

The queue length in the model in Section 8.3.1 is fractionally smaller than in the model in Section 8.3.2 for the same arrival rate and

Table 8.4. COMPARISON OF MULTISERVER BALKING MODELS

Arrival Rate per Service	Server	Utilisation	Proportion Balked	Average Queue Length	
				First Model	Second Model
1·1	2	0·466 7	0·151 4	0·079 8	0·083 3
1·5	2	0·580 9	0·225 5	0·159 6	0·169 1
1·9	2	0·670 2	0·294 5	0·260 5	0·279 8
2·1	3	0·584 2	0·165 4	0·109 7	0·115 8
2·5	3	0·653 1	0·216 3	0·169 1	0·180 2
2·9	3	0·710 1	0·265 4	0·238 5	0·256 5
3·1	4	0·645 9	0·166 5	0·121 6	0·129 1
3·5	4	0·694 8	0·205 9	0·168 6	0·180 2
3·9	4	0·736 6	0·244 6	0·221 6	0·238 4
4·1	5	0·685 4	0·164 1	0·126 4	0·134 6
4·5	5	0·723 1	0·196 5	0·165 2	0·176 9
4·9	5	0·756 0	0·228 6	0·208 1	0·224 0
5·5	6	0·744 1	0·188 3	0·161 0	0·172 6
6·5	7	0·760 5	0·181 0	0·156 7	0·168 1
7·5	8	0·773 8	0·174 6	0·152 5	0·163 7
8·5	9	0·785 0	0·168 8	0·148 5	0·159 5
9·5	10	0·794 5	0·163 7	0·144 7	0·155 5
10·5	11	0·802 8	0·159 0	0·141 3	0·151 8
11·5	12	0·810 0	0·154 8	0·138 0	0·148 3
12·5	13	0·816 5	0·150 9	0·134 9	0·145 1
13·5	14	0·822 3	0·147 3	0·132 1	0·142 0
14·5	15	0·827 5	0·144 0	0·129 4	0·139 2
15·5	16	0·832 3	0·140 9	0·126 9	0·136 5
16·5	17	0·836 6	0·138 0	0·124 5	0·134 0
17·5	18	0·840 6	0·135 3	0·122 3	0·131 6
18·5	19	0·844 4	0·132 8	0·120 2	0·129 3
19·5	20	0·847 8	0·130 5	0·118 2	0·127 2

proportion balked in each model. A difference of the same order exists between the average number in the system in the two models. Since the average waiting time is related to the average number of customers in the queue by $L = \lambda W$ the waiting times of customers in the first model will be smaller than those in the second.

As the arrival rate gets larger the proportion of customers balked gets smaller in the long term, if the number of servers is taken as the integer above the arrivals per service time. Over the range of arrival rate for which the number of servers would be fixed i.e. $n-1 < \lambda/\mu < n$ the proportion balked will increase because of the increasing load on the system. The proportion balked as λ/μ increases in unit steps by considering the behaviour of equation 8.32 can be shown to decrease very slowly to a limit of zero. If λ/μ is considered at points just below integer values $u = \lambda/n\mu$ will be approximately 1 and the proportion balked reduces to:

$$\text{proportion balked} = 1 \Big/ \left\{ e - 1 + n! \sum_0^{n-1} n^{j-n}/j! \right\}$$

using Stirling's approximation for $n! \approx (2\pi)^{1/2} n^{n+(1/2)} e^{-n}$

$$\text{Proportion balked} \approx 1 \Big/ \left[e - 1 + (2\pi n)^{1/2} \sum_0^{n-1} n^j e^{-n}/j! \right]$$

the summation can be shown to be approximately 0·5 hence

$$\text{proportion balked} \approx 1/[e - 1 + (\pi n/2)^{1/2}]$$

As n becomes large, i.e. as λ/μ becomes large this proportion will become close to zero. The number of customers balked per service time $= \lambda \times$ proportion balked$/\mu$.

$$\approx n \times \text{proportion balked} \approx n/[e - 1 + (\pi n/2)^{1/2}]$$

The number balked obviously increases as n increases even though the proportion decreases.

Example 8.3

A queueing system has customers arriving at random, and negative exponential service times, with an arrival rate per service time of 3·7. If the chance of a customer joining the queue is the reciprocal of queue size (the customer being counted in the queue for this purpose), what is the minimum number of servers required to ensure less than one per cent of customers balk at joining the queue?

This is the second multiserver model considered (Section 8.3.2) so the proportion of customers balked is given by equation 8.32.

$$\text{Proportion balked} = 1 - nU/x = 1 - U/u$$

where

$$U = uP(0) \sum_{j=0}^{n-2} x^j/j! + P(0) x^n(e^u-1)/(un!)$$

$$P(0)^{-1} = \sum_{j=0}^{n-1} x^j/j! + x^n(e^u-1)/(un!)$$

$u = x/n$ and $x = \lambda/\mu = 3.7$ in this case.

Numerical evaluation for values of n from 4 upwards gives Table 8.5.

Table 8.5.

n	4	5	6	7	8	9
u	0·925	0·7400	0·6167	0·5286	0·4625	0·4111
U	0·7165	0·6423	0·5732	0·5106	0·4556	0·4087
Proportion balked	0·2254	0·1320	0·0705	0·0341	0·0149	0·0059

9 servers are needed to ensure the proportion of customers balked is less than one percent. The utilisation of the system is 40·87% with 9 servers, the average number of customers in the queue is 0·0024 and the average number of customers in the system is 3·6807. If servers return to service in the order in which they become free, the average idle time of a server between periods of service is

$$\bar{I} = \left[1 + x \sum_{j=0}^{n-2} P(j) \middle/ \sum_{j=0}^{n-1} P(j)\right]\middle/\lambda$$

$$= 4.67 \text{ arrival intervals.}$$

The average busy period of a server from equation 8.34 is $\bar{B} = 4.67 \times$
$$\times\frac{0.4087}{0.5913} = 3.23 \text{ arrival intervals.}$$

Example 8.4

If in the last example the profit on the service of each customer is £0·1 and the cost of supplying a server is £0·02 per service time, what number of servers would give the maximum profit per service time on average?

The average number of customers served per service time is nU. The profit per service time is £0·1$n(U-0\cdot2)$. The profits for values of n from 4 to 9 are 0·206 6, 0·221 2, 0·223 9, 0·217 4, 0·204 5, 0·187 8 pounds. It is most profitable to work with 6 servers where the utilisation would be 57·32% and 7·05% of customers would balk at joining the queue.

8.3.4 Finite Balking Models

It has been seen in previous chapters the analysis of queues with limited waiting room closely parallels the development of the same type of queue with no limit on the queue size. For random arrivals of customers and negative exponential service times the recurrence relations for the steady state probabilities are usually unchanged. The limit on queue size changes the number of possible states and hence the absolute value of probabilities of these allowable states but not their ratios one to another.

The other factors of interest, average queue length, waiting time, etc., can then be derived from the steady state probabilities in the usual way. Since the models of queues with balking considered in the previous sections can be similarly analysed when there is a limit on the queue length they will not be considered here in detail but be left as an exercise for the reader.

There is one model which has been considered in the literature which is appropriate only to queues with limited waiting room and is considered below.

8.3.5 The Queue $M/M/n$ with Balking and Queue Size limited to N Customers

The chance of a customer balking at joining a queue of length j is $(j+1)/(N+1)$. If a server is free to serve a customer immediately on arrival the customer will not balk so the balking probability applies for queue lengths $j = 0, 1, \ldots, N$. The balking probability is a linear function of queue length in contrast to the geometric and inverse forms considered in previous balking models.

The steady state equations for the probabilities $P(j), j = 0, \ldots, n+N$ can be written down in the usual way and reduce to the recurrence relationships

$$P(j) = x^j P(0)/j!$$
$$0 \leqslant j \leqslant n \tag{8.36}$$

and
$$P(n+j) = u(1 - j/(N+1)) P(n+j-1)$$
$$0 \leqslant j \leqslant N$$

$$= \left(\frac{u}{N+1}\right)^j \frac{N!}{(N-j)!} P(n) \tag{8.37}$$

where $x = \lambda/\mu$, $u = x/n$,

λ = arrival rate of customers

μ = service rate of a server

n = number of servers

$P(0)$ or $P(n)$ can be found from

$$\sum_{j=0}^{n+N} P(j) = 1$$

$$P(0)^{-1} = \sum_{j=0}^{n} x^j/j! + \frac{x^n}{n!} \sum_{j=1}^{N} N! \, (u/(N+1))^j/(N-j)!$$

The proportion of customers who balk

$$= \sum_{j=0}^{N} P(n+j)(j+1)/(N+1).$$

Utilisation of system $= U = 1 - \sum_{j=0}^{n} (n-j) P(j)/n$

Average number of customers in the queue $= \sum_{j=0}^{N} jP(n+j)$

Average number of customers in the system $= \sum_{j=0}^{n+N} jP(j)$

If servers return to service in the order in which they become idle, the average idle period ($\bar{I}$) and busy period ($\bar{B}$) of a server is as usual

$$\bar{I} = \left[1 + x \sum_{j=0}^{n-2} P(j) \bigg/ \sum_{j=0}^{n-1} P(j)\right] \bigg/ \lambda$$

and
$$\bar{B} = \bar{I}U/(1-U)$$

For large values of N the system behaves like the system $M/M/n$ with no limit on the queue with the condition that the system must not be overloaded i.e. that $x < n$. If the system is overloaded then the proportion of customers who balk approaches the amount by which the system is overloaded and the utilisation of the servers approaches unity. For a basically under utilised system the proportion of customers who balk can be made as small as required by making N sufficiently large.

Example 8.5

Compare the present system for small values of N with previous balking models for $x = 2.5$ $n = 3$. The calculations are straightforward using the formulae given above. Results for the unlimited queue models discussed in the previous sections have already been calculated for the numerical values given in Table 8.4. and are given in Table 8.6 for comparison.

It has already been shown that for comparable amounts of balking the geometric model gives smaller average queue lengths than the inverse model. Table 8.6 shows the present model with limited waiting room gives a smaller average queue length than the geometric model for the same amount of balking.

Table 8.6.

$x = 2.5$ $n = 3$ N	Utilisation	Proportion Balked	Average Number in	
			Queue	*System*
0	0·598 2	0·282 1	0	1·794 6
1	0·640 5	0·231 4	0·105 2	2·026 6
2	0·662 2	0·201 7	0·203 2	2·198 9
Inverse model				
	0·653 1	0·216 3	0·180 2	2·139 6
Geometric model				
$\alpha = 0$	0·598 2	0·282 1	0	1·794 6
$\alpha = 0.429\,5$	0·640 5	0·231 4	0·121 0	2·042 4
$\alpha = 0.515\,3$	0·665 2	0·201 7	0·222 6	2·218 3

8.3.6 Other Queues with Balking

Most of the early work on queues with balking was on single server queues. Haight[24, 25] considered the case $M/M/1$ with general form of balking. Finch[26] studied the case $GI/M/1$ with customers departing without service (reneging) when their waiting time reaches a limit. A similar form of reneging was considered by Ghosal[27] for the queue $D/G/1$. Ancker and Gafarian[28, 29] looked at the queue $M/M/1$ with both balking and reneging with limited waiting room. This work was extended by Rao[30, 31] to the queue $M/G/1$ with breakdowns in the serivice facility. Daley[32] considered the most general form of single server queue $GI/G/1$ with a general form of customer impatience and obtained an equation for the waiting time of customers.

Singh[33] compared $M/M/2$ with a fixed probability of balking at a queue with a similar queue where the average service times of the two servers were different, at the same utilisation. Morse[34] considered the geometric multiserver model but did not give results as extensive as those given above.

CHAPTER 9

Priority Queues

All queues studied in previous chapters have had the queue discipline first come first served. This chapter considers other queue disciplines and their effect on customer waiting time. Interest in this topic has been aroused in the scheduling of jobs on high speed digital computers in an attempt to minimise customer delays. The effect of priorities is considered by Morse[34] for two classes of customers one having priority for service over the other class. Later work was done by Cox and Smith[4] for more than two classes of priority and a volume entirely on queues with priority queue discipline by Jaiswal[35] covers the topic extensively. The purpose of this chapter is to summarise the main results obtained so far.

The commonest form of priority discipline considered has been that of the customers being divided into p groups numbered 1 to p, customers of group j having priority of service over customers in groups above j. Within each of the p groups the queue discipline is usually first come first served. A further division in the queues considered has been that of whether service of a low priority customer should be interrupted, or pre-empted when a customer of higher priority arrives. The case where the low priority customer returns to the head of the queue of customers of his own priority group and service commences on the higher priority arrival has been called pre-emptive priority. The case where the service of a customer is allowed to finish even though customers of higher priority have arrived during the service is called non pre-emptive priority.

9.1 $M/G/1$ WITH NON PRE-EMPTIVE PRIORITY

Cobham[36] considered this queue with p priority classes of customer all classes having the same distribution of service time and obtained the formula for average waiting time:

$$W_r = \frac{\frac{1}{2}\lambda \int_0^\infty t^2 f(t)\, \mathrm{d}t}{(1-s_{r-1})(1-s_r)} \tag{9.1}$$

where W_r = the average waiting time of customers in the rth priority class.

$$s_r = \sum_{j=0}^r \lambda_j/\mu \qquad s_0 = 0$$

$f(t)$ = p.d.f. of service time t

$1/\mu = \int_0^\infty tf(t)\, \mathrm{d}t$ = average service time

λ_j = arrival rate of customers of the jth priority group

$$\lambda = \sum_{j=0}^p \lambda_j$$

Cox and Smith[4] generalised this result to the case where each priority group has its own service time distribution.

$f_j(t)$ = the p.d.f. of service time t of the jth priority group

$$b_j = \int_0^\infty tf_j(t)\, \mathrm{d}t \quad \text{and} \quad c_j = \int_0^\infty t^2 f_j(t)\, \mathrm{d}t$$

If the time scale is chosen so that $\lambda = \sum_{j=1}^p \lambda_j = 1$

then the utilisation of the system $= \varrho = \sum_{j=1}^p \lambda_j b_j$

If $c = \sum_{j=0}^p \lambda_j c_j$ then the average waiting time of customers of priority r is

$$W_r = \frac{\frac{1}{2}c}{(1-s_{r-1})(1-s_r)} \tag{9.2}$$

where $$s_r = \sum_{j=0}^{r} \lambda_j b_j \qquad s_0 = 0$$

which can easily be seen to reduce to equation 9.1 when all service time distributions are identical.

9.1.1 Optimum Priority Ordering

Cox and Smith go on to consider the best priority order of the p groups when the cost of unit waiting time for a customer in the jth group is d_j, that is the priority order which will minimise the average cost of waiting,

average delay cost $= \sum_{j=1}^{p} \lambda_j d_j W_j$

They show that if the groups are ordered in increasing order of the ratio b_j/d_j the average cost will be minimised.

A special case of this is that when all customer waiting time costs (d_j) are equal. The average delay is minimised for this case when the priorities are in order of average service time of the groups, customers having the smallest average waiting time being given the highest priority.

The extreme for this priority classification is when p becomes infinite and customers are served strictly in order of their service times. The average waiting time in this case is the minimum possible and is shown by Cox and Smith to be

$$W_{\min} = \frac{c}{2} \int_0^\infty \frac{f(t)\,\mathrm{d}t}{\left[1 - \int_0^t u f(u)\,\mathrm{d}u \right]^2} \qquad (9.3)$$

Example 9.1

Compare the average waiting times for the queue with service time distribution

$$f(t) = \frac{1}{2b} \qquad 0 \leqslant t \leqslant 2b$$

when queue disciplines are first come first served and shortest service time first respectively.

The average waiting time in the queue when queue discipline is first come first served is

$$W = \frac{b\varrho}{2(1-\varrho)} \int \frac{t^2 f(t)\, dt}{b^2} = \frac{2b\varrho}{3(1-\varrho)}$$

On the shortest service time first discipline the average waiting time from equation 9.3 is

$$W_{min} = \frac{2b^2}{3} \int_0^{2b} \frac{dt}{2b\left[1 - \dfrac{t^2}{4b}\right]^2} \qquad b < 1$$

$$= \frac{b}{3} \int_0^{2b} \frac{dt}{\left[1 - \dfrac{t}{2b^{1/2}}\right]^2 \left[1 + \dfrac{t}{2b^{1/2}}\right]^2}$$

$$= \frac{b}{3} \int_0^{2b} \frac{1}{4}\left(\frac{1}{\left(1 - \dfrac{t}{a}\right)} + \frac{1}{\left(1 - \dfrac{t}{a}\right)^2} + \frac{1}{\left(1 + \dfrac{t}{a}\right)} + \frac{1}{\left(1 + \dfrac{t}{a}\right)^2}\right) dt$$

$$a = \frac{1}{2b^{1/2}}$$

$$= \frac{b^{3/2}}{6}\left\{\log_e\left(\frac{1 + b^{1/2}}{1 - b^{1/2}}\right) + \frac{2b^{1/2}}{(1 - b)}\right\}$$

when the arrival rate is taken as unity $\varrho = b$.

so $$W = \frac{2b^2}{3(1-b)} \qquad b < 1$$

numerical comparisons give Table 9.1.

The ratio of W_{min} to W decreases as utilisation increases showing the proportionate saving increases with the utilisation.

Oliver and Pestalozzi[37] considered the problem of dividing the service time distribution into non overlapping intervals in such a way

Table 9.1.

b	W	W_{min}	W_{min}/W
0·1	0·0074	0·0072	0·9670
0·2	0·0333	0·0310	0·9313
0·3	0·0857	0·0765	0·8932
0·4	0·1778	0·1518	0·8535
0·5	0·3333	0·2705	0·8117
0·6	0·6000	0·4598	0·7664
0·7	1·0889	0·7806	0·7169
0·8	2·1333	1·4110	0·6614
0·9	5·4000	3·2176	0·5958

that the average waiting time over all customers would be minimised for $N+1$ such classes if the classes in increasing order are treated as customers with decreasing priority. Formulae to obtain the optimum division into priority classes are obtained and numerical results given for a few special cases. Cox and Smith considered the same problem for two priority classes and a negative exponential distribution of service time. Taking the average arrival interval to be the unit of time and the average service time as b (< 1), the point at which the division between priority 1 and priority 2 customers occurs (rb) is found by Cox and Smith to be

$$1/b = 1 + e^{-r}/(r-1) \qquad (9.4)$$

for minimum average delay to customers.

Customers with service times less than rb are given higher priority than customers whose times are greater than rb. Within each group the discipline is first come first served.

9.1.2 Further Results for $M/G/1$ when all Priority Groups have the same Service Distribution

Higher moments of the waiting time distribution of each priority group are considered by Kesten and Runnenburg[38] for this case and they find the second moment about the origin to be, for the rth priority group,

$$E(W_r^2) = \lambda\mu^{(3)}/[3(1-s_{r-1})(1-s_r)]$$

$$+\lambda\mu^{(2)}\sum_{j=1}^{r}\lambda_j\mu^{(2)}/[2(1-s_{r-1})^2(1-s_r)^2]$$

$$+\lambda\mu^{(2)}\sum_{j=1}^{r-1}\lambda_j\mu^{(2)}/[2(1-s_{r-1})^3(1-s_r)] \qquad (9.5)$$

where $\mu^{(2)} =$ 2nd moment of service time about the origin
$$= \int t^2 f(t)\,dt$$

$\mu^{(3)} =$ 3rd moment of service time about the origin
$$= \int t^3 f(t)\,dt$$

λ_j = the arrival rate of customers of group j

$$s_r = \sum_{j=1}^{r}\lambda_j/\mu \qquad s_0 = 0 \qquad \lambda = \sum_{j=1}^{p}\lambda_j$$

$$r = 1, 2, \ldots, p.$$

The first two moments of waiting time given by equation 9.1 and 9.5 while not describing the distribution of waiting time completely are the moments of greatest practical importance, giving the average and the spread about the average.

As the system is a single server one the utilisation of the server is

$\varrho = \lambda/\mu$ where $\lambda = \sum_{j=1}^{p}\lambda_j =$ the overall arrival rate of all groups of customers, and $\mu =$ the average service rate $= 1/b$.

The chance a customer will not have to wait for service is the chance the server is idle, $(1-\varrho)$.

The average waiting time for all groups of customers is

$$W = \sum_{r=1}^{p}\frac{\lambda_r W_r}{\lambda}$$

where W_r is given in equation 9.1, the value of W can easily be reduced to

$$W = \frac{\mu^{(2)}}{2(1-\varrho)} \qquad (9.6)$$

which is identical to Kendall's formula for average waiting time in the queue $M/G/1$ without priorities. So a priority system which is not dependent on the service time in some way will not alter the overall average waiting time.

Because of the relationship between the average waiting time and the average number of customers in the queue the result on waiting time means the average number of customers in the queue is also unchanged.

The arrivals are random, so the average busy period of the server can be found by the usual argument to be $b/(1-\varrho)$. The distribution of busy period will also be unchanged by the priority system and will be the same as for the queue $M/G/1$ without priorities.

These results do not of course apply when the service time distribution of the priority groups differ.

9.2 THE QUEUE $M/M/n$ WITH PRIORITY CUSTOMERS

The study of multiserver queues with priority customers is more difficult for the more general form of arrival and service time distributions as can be seen from Jaiswal[35]. Some results have been obtained for the simple queue $M/M/n$ with priority customers. Cobham[36] considers the multiserver queue with p priority classes of customers. Customers of class j have priority over customers with priority greater than j. The priority is non pre-emptive so customers being served do not have their service broken into if customers of higher priority arrive during their service. Within a priority class the customers are served in the order first come first served. Cobham shows the average waiting time for customers of priority r is

$$W_r = \frac{c/n\mu}{(1-s_{r-1})(1-s_r)} \tag{9.7}$$

$$r = 1, 2, \ldots, p$$

where $\quad s_r = \sum_{j=1}^{r} \lambda_j/n\mu; \quad \lambda_j = $ arrival rate of jth priority class

$\mu = $ service rate of a server

$n = $ number of servers

and

$$c = x^n \left/ \left\{ n! \, (1-u) \left[\sum_{j=0}^{n-1} x^j/j! + \sum_{j=n}^{\infty} x^j/n! \, n^{j-n} \right] \right\} \right.$$

$$x = \lambda/\mu, \quad u = x/n.$$

Since the priority system is not related to the service time the average waiting time over all customers should be the same as for $M/M/n$ with the same utilisation.

The chance a customer of any priority does not have to wait is $\sum_{j=0}^{n-1} P(j)$ where the steady state probabilities $P(j)$ are given by

$$\left. \begin{aligned} P(j) &= P(0) \, x^j/j! & j \leqslant n \\ P(j) &= P(0) \, x^j/n! \, n^{j-n} & j \geqslant n \end{aligned} \right\} \tag{9.8}$$

Since the number of customers in the system is unchanged by the allocation of a priority to the individual the steady state probabilities are identical to those for the queue $M/M/n$ without priorities.

The average length of busy period can similarly be argued to be identical to that for the queue $M/M/n$ already studied.

9.3. SOME OTHER PRIORITY QUEUES

9.3.1 Pre-emptive Queue Discipline

The most comprehensive study of queues with customers having priority is that of Jaiswal[35]. The most usual variation on the priority rules considered so far is that of pre-emptive priority where service of customers is interrupted if a customer of higher priority arrives. Customers within a priority class are served in the order of arrival. Customers of the highest priority in such a queue will not be affected at all by customers of lower priority and so results for these customers can be found by treating them as the only customers to the system. All other priority customers will have the likelihood of their service being interrupted by higher priority customers and this type of queue is further subdivided into one in which the service continues from the point at which it was broken off—pre-emptive resume priority, or into one in which the service recommences from the beginning—pre-emptive repeat priority. The results for these types of queues will depend on whether the interrupted service is resumed or repeated for most forms of service time distribution. The only case where there will be no difference in the two policies will be that of negative exponential service times. For this distribution the remainder of a service time has the same distribution as a full service time so the pre-emptive resume policy will be no different from the pre-emptive repeat policy. Brosh[39] considers the queue $M/M/n$ with pre-emptive priorities gives upper and lower bounds for waiting time for any priority class and the average wait prior to the initial service commencing. Further waits are then necessary if the service is interrupted by a customer or customers of higher priority. Segal[40] gives the first two moments of waiting time for each priority group in the queue.

9.3.2 Time Sharing Queues

The introduction of the use of remote consoles and time sharing system on computers has lead to the study of queueing models for this type of system. Adiri and Avi-Itzhak[41] consider the queue $M/M/1$ in which each customer is given a constant length of time for service and if service is not complete at the end of this time the customer goes to the end of the queue. The fixed time is split into two parts, a set up time and a service time. The effect of the length of time the server is available to a customer on the time the customer is in the system is given numerically in a particular case. The same authors[42] considered a similar queue $M/M/1$ where customers on arrival join a queue of highest priority and obtain a service time of θ_1; if service is not complete they join a lower priority queue and obtain a service time of θ_2. The process is repeated until the full service has been obtained; the number of priority groups considered is r and customers whose service is not complete on reaching the rth priority class repeatedly join this priority queue until service is complete.

Schrage[43] considers the queue $M/G/1$ with priority classes, set up times for interrupted service and considers means and variances of delays. Chang[44] considers $M/G_p/1$ with priorities, the service time distribution being different for each priority class. The service is also divided into two parts one of which has priority over the other, these being equivalent to communication and processing in the computer system.

Several other priority disciplines are considered by Jaiswal[35]. First, alternating priorities in which the type of customer currently being served has highest priority, a change in priority occurring whenever one group has finished service. Second, dynamic priority disciplines in which the priorities changed according to the state of the customers in the queue, length of waiting time elapsed. Third, cut off priorities where some priority groups are not allowed to start service if more than a given number of servers are busy. For further details on such systems the reader is referred to Jaiswal.

Table A.1. AVERAGE WAITING OF CUSTOMERS IN THE QUEUE $M/M/n$, IN UNITS OF AVERAGE SERVICE TIME

Utilisation (u)	Number of Servers (n)								
	2	3	4	5	6	7	8	9	10
0·1	0·0101	0·0014	0·0002	0·0000	0·0000	0·0000	0·0000	0·0000	0·0000
0·2	0·0417	0·0103	0·0030	0·0010	0·0003	0·0001	0·0000	0·0000	0·0000
0·3	0·0989	0·0333	0·0132	0·0058	0·0027	0·0013	0·0006	0·0003	0·0002
0·4	0·1905	0·0784	0·0378	0·0199	0·0111	0·0064	0·0039	0·0024	0·0015
0·5	0·3333	0·1579	0·0870	0·0521	0·0330	0·0218	0·0148	0·0102	0·0072
0·6	0·5625	0·2956	0·1794	0·1181	0·0819	0·0589	0·0436	0·0330	0·0253
0·7	0·9608	0·5470	0·3572	0·2519	0·1867	0·1432	0·1128	0·0906	0·0739
0·8	1·7778	1·0787	0·7455	0·5541	0·4315	0·3471	0·2860	0·2401	0·2046
0·9	4·2632	2·7235	1·9693	1·5250	1·2335	1·0285	0·8769	0·7606	0·6687

$$\text{utilisation} = \frac{\text{Av. Service Time}}{(n \times \text{Av. Arrival Interval})}$$

n = number of servers

Table A.2. AVERAGE WAITING TIME OF CUSTOMERS IN THE QUEUE $M/D/n$ (IN UNITS OF AVERAGE SERVICE TIME)

Utilisation (u)	Number of Servers (n)								
	2	3	4	5	6	7	8	9	10
0·1	0·0062	0·0009	0·0002	0·0000	0·0000	0·0000	0·0000	0·0000	0·0000
0·2	0·0242	0·0066	0·0021	0·0007	0·0002	0·0001	0·0000	0·0000	0·0000
0·3	0·0553	0·0201	0·0085	0·0039	0·0019	0·0009	0·0005	0·0002	0·0001
0·4	0·1033	0·0450	0·0227	0·0124	0·0072	0·0043	0·0026	0·0017	0·0011
0·5	0·1767	0·0872	0·0497	0·0307	0·0199	0·0135	0·0093	0·0066	0·0047
0·6	0·2930	0·1584	0·0984	0·0661	0·0467	0·0342	0·0257	0·0197	0·0154
0·7	0·4936	0·2862	0·1897	0·1355	0·1016	0·0788	0·0627	0·0508	0·0419
0·8	0·9030	0·5537	0·3860	0·2890	0·2265	0·1833	0·1519	0·1282	0·1098
0·9	2·0138	1·2887	0·9340	0·7237	0·5848	0·4894	0·4164	0·3606	0·3175

Table A.3. AVERAGE WAITING TIME OF CUSTOMERS IN THE QUEUE $D/M/n$ (IN UNITS OF AVERAGE SERVICE TIME)

Utilisation (u)	Number of Servers (n)								
	2	3	4	5	6	7	8	9	10
0·1	0·0000	0·0000	0·0000	0·0000	0·0000	0·0000	0·0000	0·0000	0·0000
0·2	0·0003	0·0000	0·0000	0·0000	0·0000	0·0000	0·0000	0·0000	0·0000
0·3	0·0048	0·0008	0·0002	0·0000	0·0000	0·0000	0·0000	0·0000	0·0000
0·4	0·0223	0·0060	0·0019	0·0007	0·0002	0·0001	0·0000	0·0000	0·0000
0·5	0·0649	0·0239	0·0103	0·0049	0·0024	0·0013	0·0007	0·0004	0·0002
0·6	0·1520	0·0685	0·0360	0·0206	0·0125	0·0079	0·0051	0·0034	0·0023
0·7	0·3257	0·1696	0·1020	0·0665	0·0458	0·0327	0·0240	0·0180	0·0137
0·8	0·7111	0·4114	0·2725	0·1947	0·1461	0·1134	0·0903	0·0734	0·0605
0·9	1·9330	1·2112	0·8612	0·6567	0·5238	0·4310	0·3629	0·3110	0·2703

utilisation = Average Service Time/($n \cdot$ Average Arrival Interval)

Table A.4. AVERAGE WAITING TIME OF CUSTOMERS IN THE QUEUE $E_2/E_2/n$ (IN UNITS OF AVERAGE SERVICE TIME)

Utilisation (u)	Number of Servers (n)								
	2	3	4	5	6	7	8	9	10
0·1	0·0006	0·0000	0·0000	0·0000	0·0000	0·0000	0·0000	0·0000	0·0000
0·2	0·0065	0·0011	0·0002	0·0000	0·0000	0·0000	0·0000	0·0000	0·0000
0·3	0·0235	0·0062	0·0019	0·0007	0·0002	0·0001	0·0000	0·0000	0·0000
0·4	0·0576	0·0205	0·0085	0·0039	0·0019	0·0009	0·0005	0·0003	0·0001
0·5	0·1181	0·0512	0·0253	0·0142	0·0082	0·0050	0·0031	0·0020	0·0013
0·6	0·2222	0·1103	0·0639	0·0400	0·0265	0·0182	0·0128	0·0093	0·0069
0·7	0·4125	0·2275	0·1441	0·0988	0·0712	0·0532	0·0407	0·0319	0·0258
0·8*	0·83	0·46	0·33	0·23	0·19	0·14	0·12	0·09	0·09
0·9*	2·0	1·20	0·92	0·65	0·57	0·44	0·40	0·32	0·30

* The figures for these values of utilisation were obtained by simulation.

155

Table A.5. AVERAGE WAITING TIME, IN UNITS OF AVERAGE SERVICE TIME, FOR THE SINGLE SERVER QUEUE $E_k/E_l/1$ WITH UTILISATION $u = 0.1$

$v_a = 1/k$	Value of l for the Erlang Service Distribution $= 1/v_s$									
	1	2	3	4	5	6	7	8	9	10
0·1	0·0010	0·0001	0·0001	0·0004	0·0007	0·0012	0·0018	0·0025	0·0033	0·0040
0·2	0·0042	0·0010	0·0004	0·0003	0·0033	0·0002	0·0006	0·0015	0·0076	0·0093
0·3	0·0102	0·0038	0·0023	0·0017	0·0014	0·0012	0·0011	0·0010	0·0010	0·0009
0·4	0·0189	0·0090	0·0064	0·0052	0·0046	0·0042	0·0039	0·0037	0·0035	0·0034
0·5	0·0301	0·0166	0·0128	0·0110	0·0100	0·0093	0·0088	0·0085	0·0082	0·0080
0·6	0·0433	0·0265	0·0214	0·0190	0·0176	0·0167	0·0160	0·0155	0·0151	0·0148
0·7	0·0582	0·0384	0·0321	0·0291	0·0273	0·0261	0·0253	0·0247	0·0242	0·0238
0·8	0·0747	0·0520	0·0446	0·0410	0·0389	0·0374	0·0364	0·0357	0·0351	0·0346
0·9	0·0924	0·0670	0·0587	0·0545	0·0521	0·0504	0·0492	0·0484	0·0477	0·0471
1·0	0·1111	0·0833	0·0741	0·0694	0·0667	0·0648	0·0639	0·0625	0·0617	0·0611

Table A.5. (continued) AVERAGE WAITING TIME, IN UNITS OF AVERAGE SERVICE TIME, FOR THE SINGLE SERVER QUEUE $E_k/E_l/1$ WITH UTILISATION $u = 0.2$

$v_a = 1/k$	Value of l for the Erlang Service Distribution $= 1/v_s$									
	1	2	3	4	5	6	7	8	9	10
0·1	0·0188	0·0035	0·0013	0·0006	0·0003	0·0002	0·0040	0·0098	0·0109	0·0051
0·2	0·0353	0·0116	0·0064	0·0044	0·0033	0·0027	0·0024	0·0021	0·0019	0·0017
0·3	0·0554	0·0243	0·0162	0·0127	0·0107	0·0095	0·0087	0·0081	0·0076	0·0073
0·4	0·0783	0·0408	0·0301	0·0252	0·0223	0·0205	0·0193	0·0183	0·0176	0·0171
0·5	0·1035	0·0604	0·0474	0·0412	0·0376	0·0353	0·0336	0·0324	0·0315	0·0307
0·6	0·1304	0·0825	0·0675	0·0602	0·0559	0·0531	0·0511	0·0497	0·0485	0·0476
0·7	0·1588	0·1065	0·0898	0·0816	0·0767	0·0735	0·0712	0·0695	0·0682	0·0671
0·8	0·1883	0·1322	0·1140	0·1049	0·0996	0·0960	0·0934	0·0915	0·0901	0·0889
0·9	0·2187	0·1593	0·1397	0·1299	0·1241	0·1202	0·1174	0·1153	0·1137	0·1124
1·0	0·2500	0·1875	0·1667	0·1563	0·1500	0·1458	0·1429	0·1406	0·1389	0·1375

Table A.5. (continued) AVERAGE WAITING TIME, IN UNITS OF AVERAGE SERVICE TIME, FOR THE SINGLE SERVER QUEUE $E_k/E_l/1$ WITH UTILISATION $u = 0.3$

$v_s = 1/k$	Value of 1 for the Erlang Service Distribution, $= 1/v_s$									
	1	2	3	4	5	6	7	8	9	10
0·1	0·0714	0·0202	0·0093	0·0054	0·0035	0·0025	0·0019	0·0016	0·0053	0·0045
0·2	0·1040	0·0415	0·0253	0·0184	0·0148	0·0125	0·0110	0·0099	0·0091	0·0085
0·3	0·1396	0·0679	0·0475	0·0382	0·0329	0·0296	0·0273	0·0256	0·0243	0·0233
0·4	0·1773	0·0980	0·0742	0·0629	0·0564	0·0522	0·0492	0·0470	0·0453	0·0440
0·5	0·2166	0·1310	0·1043	0·0914	0·0839	0·0789	0·0755	0·0729	0·0708	0·0693
0·6	0·2573	0·1661	0·1371	0·1229	0·1145	0·1090	0·1050	0·1021	0·0998	0·0980
0·7	0·2990	0·2031	0·1720	0·1567	0·1476	0·1415	0·1372	0·1340	0·1315	0·1296
0·8	0·3415	0·2414	0·2086	0·1923	0·1826	0·1761	0·1715	0·1681	0·1654	0·1633
0·9	0·3848	0·2809	0·2466	0·2295	0·2192	0·2124	0·2075	0·2039	0·2010	0·1988
1·0	0·4286	0·3214	0·2857	0·2679	0·2571	0·2500	0·2449	0·2411	0·2381	0·2357

Table A.5. (continued) AVERAGE WAITING TIME, IN UNITS OF AVERAGE SERVICE TIME, FOR THE SINGLE SERVER QUEUE $E_k/E_l/1$ WITH UTILISATION $u = 0.4$

Value of I for the Erlang Service Distribution = $1/v_s$

$v_a = 1/k$	1	2	3	4	5	6	7	8	9	10
0·1	0,1679	0·0596	0·0320	0·0207	0·0149	0·0115	0·0093	0·0078	0·0067	0·0059
0·2	0·2183	0·0979	0·0639	0·0485	0·0400	0·0346	0·0310	0·0283	0·0263	0·0248
0·3	0·2707	0·1408	0·1018	0·0836	0·0731	0·0663	0·0615	0·0580	0·0554	0·0533
0·4	0·3247	0·1869	0·1441	0·1236	0·1116	0·1037	0·0982	0·0941	0·0909	0·0884
0·5	0·3799	0·2355	0·1896	0·1672	0·1541	0·1454	0·1392	0·1346	0·1311	0·1283
0·6	0·4360	0·2859	0·2374	0·2136	0·1995	0·1901	0·1835	0·1785	0·1747	0·1716
0·7	0·4929	0·3378	0·2872	0·2622	0·2472	0·2373	0·2303	0·2250	0·2209	0·2176
0·8	0·5503	0·3909	0·3385	0·3124	0·2968	0·2864	0·2790	0·2735	0·2692	0·2657
0·9	0·6083	0·4451	0·3909	0·3640	0·3478	0·3370	0·3293	0·3236	0·3191	0·3155
1·0	0·6667	0·5000	0·4444	0·4167	0·4000	0·3889	0·3810	0·3750	0·3704	0·3667

Table A.5. (continued) AVERAGE WAITING TIME, IN UNITS OF AVERAGE SERVICE TIME, FOR THE SINGLE SERVER QUEUE $E_k/E_l/1$ WITH UTILISATION $u = 0.5$

$v_a = 1/k$	Value of l for the Erlang Service Distribution $= 1/v_s$									
	1	2	3	4	5	6	7	8	9	10
0·1	0·3246	0·1326	0·0785	0·0545	0·0415	0·0336	0·0282	0·0245	0·0217	0·0195
0·2	0·3962	0·1924	0·1313	0·1029	0·0867	0·0763	0·0691	0·0638	0·0598	0·0566
0·3	0·4692	0·2559	0·1897	0·1581	0·1396	0·1276	0·1192	0·1129	0·1081	0·1043
0·4	0·5432	0·3221	0·2520	0·2150	0·1978	0·1846	0·1753	0·1683	0·1630	0·1587
0·5	0·6180	0·3904	0·3170	0·2810	0·2597	0·2456	0·2356	0·2281	0·2223	0·2177
0·6	0·6935	0·4602	0·3842	0·3467	0·3243	0·3095	0·2990	0·2911	0·2850	0·2801
0·7	0·7696	0·5313	0·4531	0·4142	0·3911	0·3756	0·3647	0·3564	0·3501	0·3450
0·8	0·8460	0·6034	0·5232	0·4833	0·4594	0·4435	0·4322	0·4237	0·4171	0·4118
0·9	0·9229	0·6764	0·5945	0·5537	0·5292	0·5129	0·5012	0·4925	0·4857	0·4803
1·0	1·0000	0·7500	0·6667	0·6250	0·6000	0·5833	0·5714	0·5625	0·5556	0·5500

Table A.5. (continued) AVERAGE WAITING TIME, IN UNITS OF AVERAGE SERVICE TIME, FOR THE SINGLE SERVER QUEUE $E_k/E_l/1$ WITH UTILISATION $u = 0.6$

$v_a = 1/k$	Value of l for the Erlang Service Distribution $= 1/v_s$									
	1	2	3	4	5	6	7	8	9	10
0·1	0·5786	0·2600	0·1643	0·1200	0·0951	0·0793	0·0684	0·0606	0·0547	0·0501
0·2	0·6786	0·3488	0·2463	0·1973	0·1689	0·1504	0·1375	0·1280	0·1207	0·1149
0·3	0·7796	0·4407	0·3330	0·2808	0·2500	0·2299	0·2156	0·2050	0·1968	0·1903
0·4	0·8813	0·5348	0·4232	0·3684	0·3360	0·3146	0·2994	0·2880	0·2793	0·2723
0·5	0·9835	0·6306	0·5157	0·4590	0·4253	0·4029	0·3870	0·3751	0·3659	0·3586
0·6	1·0862	0·7278	0·6102	0·5519	0·5171	0·4940	0·4775	0·4652	0·4556	0·4480
0·7	1·1892	0·8259	0·7061	0·6465	0·6108	0·5871	0·5702	0·5576	0·5477	0·5399
0·8	1·2926	0·9249	0·8031	0·7424	0·7061	0·6819	0·6646	0·6516	0·6416	0·6335
0·9	1·3962	1·0247	0·9012	0·8395	0·8025	0·7778	0·7603	0·7471	0·7369	0·7287
1·0	1·5000	1·1250	1·0000	0·9375	0·9000	0·8750	0·8571	0·8438	0·8333	0·8250

Table A.5. (continued) AVERAGE WAITING TIME, IN UNITS OF AVERAGE SERVICE TIME, FOR THE SINGLE SERVER QUEUE $E_k/E_l/1$ WITH UTILISATION $u = 0.7$

$v_a = 1/k$	Value of l for the Erlang Service Distribution $= 1/v_s$									
	1	2	3	4	5	6	7	8	9	10
0·1	1·0198	0·4908	0·3252	0·2462	0·2006	0·1711	0·1506	0·1355	0·1240	0·1150
0·2	1·1642	0·6248	0·4526	0·3689	0·3198	0·2876	0·2649	0·2480	0·2350	0·2247
0·3	1·3093	0·7612	0·5840	0·4970	0·4456	0·4116	0·3875	0·3695	0·3556	0·3445
0·4	1·4548	0·8994	0·7183	0·6288	0·5756	0·5404	0·5153	0·4966	0·4821	0·4705
0·5	1·6006	1·0391	0·8547	0·7633	0·7088	0·6726	0·6468	0·6275	0·6125	0·6005
0·6	1·7468	1·1798	0·9927	0·8997	0·8442	0·8072	0·7808	0·7611	0·7458	0·7335
0·7	1·8932	1·3214	1·1321	1·0378	0·9813	0·9437	0·9169	0·8968	0·8812	0·8687
0·8	2·0397	1·4637	1·2724	1·1770	1·1198	1·0817	1·0545	1·0342	1·0183	1·0056
0·9	2·1865	1·6066	1·4136	1·3172	1·2595	1·2209	1·1934	1·1728	1·1568	1·1439
1·0	2·3333	1·7500	1·5556	1·4583	1·4000	1·3611	1·3333	1·3125	1·2963	1·2833

Table A.5. (continued) AVERAGE WAITING TIME, IN UNITS OF AVERAGE SERVICE TIME, FOR THE SINGLE SERVER QUEUE $E_k/E_l/1$ WITH UTILISATION $u = 0.8$

$v_a = 1/k$	Value of l for the Erlang Service Distribution $= 1/v_s$									
	1	2	3	4	5	6	7	8	9	10
0·1	1·9222	0·9744	0·6692	0·5205	0·3916	0·3758	0·3355	0·3056	0·2826	0·2644
0·2	2·1523	1·1947	0·8831	0·7299	0·6391	0·5791	0·5366	0·5049	0·4803	0·4608
0·3	2·3826	1·4168	1·1005	0·9440	0·8509	0·7891	0·7452	0·7124	0·6869	0·6667
0·4	2·6132	1·6405	1·3203	1·1614	1·0665	1·0035	0·9586	0·9250	0·8989	0·8781
0·5	2·8440	1·8653	1·5419	1·3811	1·2849	1·2209	1·1753	1·1411	1·1146	1·0934
0·6	3·0750	2·0910	1·7650	1·6026	1·5053	1·4406	1·3944	1·3598	1·3329	1·3114
0·7	3·3061	2·3174	1·9892	1·8254	1·7273	1·6620	1·6153	1·5804	1·5532	1·5315
0·8	3·5373	2·5444	2·2143	2·0494	1·9506	1·8847	1·8377	1·8025	1·7750	1·7531
0·9	3·7686	2·7720	2·4402	2·2743	2·1749	2·1086	2·0612	2·0257	1·9981	1·9760
1·0	4·0000	3·0000	2·6667	2·5000	2·4000	2·3333	2·2857	2·2500	2·2222	2·2000

Table A.5. (continued) AVERAGE WAITING TIME, IN UNITS OF AVERAGE SERVICE TIME, FOR THE SINGLE SERVER QUEUE $E_k/E_1/1$ WITH UTILISATION $u = 0.9$

$v_s = 1/k$	Value of l for the Erlang Service Distribution $= 1/v_s$									
	1	2	3	4	5	6	7	8	9	10
0·1	4·660 3	2·460 2	1·737 4	1·380 0	1·167 4	1·026 6	0·926 7	0·852 2	0·794 4	0·748 4
0·2	5·142 1	2·933 0	2·204 2	1·842 4	1·626 5	1·483 1	1·381 1	1·304 7	1·245 4	1·198 1
0·3	5·624 1	3·407 2	2·673 8	2·308 9	2·090 7	1·945 6	1·842 2	1·764 7	1·704 5	1·656 4
0·4	6·106 1	3·882 7	3·145 6	2·778 3	2·558 4	2·412 0	2·307 6	2·229 4	2·168 5	2·119 9
0·5	6·588 3	4·359 0	3·618 9	3·249 7	3·028 5	2·881 1	2·776 0	2·697 2	2·635 9	2·586 9
0·6	7·070 5	4·836 2	4·093 5	3·722 7	3·500 4	3·352 3	3·246 6	3·167 4	3·105 8	3·056 5
0·7	7·552 8	5·313 9	4·569 0	4·196 9	3·973 8	3·825 1	3·718 9	3·639 3	3·577 4	3·527 9
0·8	8·035 2	5·792 2	5·045 4	4·672 2	4·448 3	4·299 1	4·192 6	4·112 7	4·050 5	4·000 8
0·9	8·517 6	6·270 9	5·522 4	5·148 2	4·923 8	4·774 1	4·667 3	4·587 1	4·524 8	4·475 0
1·0	9·000 0	6·750 0	6·000 0	5·625 0	5·400 0	5·250 0	5·142 9	5·062 5	5·000 0	4·950 0

Table A.6. THE CHANCE A CUSTOMER DOES NOT HAVE TO WAIT FOR SERVICE IN THE QUEUE $M/M/n$

Utilisation (u)	Number of Servers (n)								
	2	3	4	5	6	7	8	9	10
0·1	0·9818	0·9963	0·9992	0·9998	—	—	—	—	—
0·2	0·9333	0·9753	0·9904	0·9962	0·9984	0·9994	0·9997	0·9999	—
0·3	0·8615	0·9300	0·9630	0·9799	0·9889	0·9938	0·9965	0·9980	0·9988
0·4	0·7714	0·8588	0·9093	0·9403	0·9600	0·9729	0·9815	0·9873	0·9912
0·5	0·6667	0·7632	0·8261	0·8696	0·9009	0·9238	0·9410	0·9540	0·9639
0·6	0·5500	0·6453	0·7130	0·7638	0·8034	0·8349	0·8605	0·8814	0·8987
0·7	0·4235	0·5077	0·5713	0·6222	0·6640	0·6993	0·7294	0·7555	0·7783
0·8	0·2889	0·3528	0·4036	0·4459	0·4822	0·5141	0·5424	0·5678	0·5908
0·9	0·1474	0·1829	0·2122	0·2375	0·2599	0·2800	0·2985	0·3155	0·3313

(Note: when the chance is 1·0000 the entry in the table is —
utilisation = Average Service Time$/(n \times$ Average Arrival Interval)

Table A.7. THE CHANCE A CUSTOMER DOES NOT HAVE TO WAIT FOR SERVICE IN THE QUEUE $M/D/n$

Utilisation (u)	Number of Servers (n)								
	2	3	4	5	6	7	8	9	10
0·1	0·9822	0·9964	0·9992	0·9998	1·0000	1·0000	1·0000	1·0000	1·0000
0·2	0·9355	0·9764	0·9908	0·9963	0·9985	0·9994	0·9997	0·9999	1·0000
0·3	0·8664	0·9335	0·9651	0·9810	0·9895	0·9941	0·9966	0·9981	0·9989
0·4	0·7792	0·8662	0·9150	0·9443	0·9629	0·9749	0·9828	0·9881	0·9918
0·5	0·6767	0·7747	0·8367	0·8787	0·9083	0·9298	0·9457	0·9577	0·9669
0·6	0·5613	0·6602	0·7285	0·7788	0·8173	0·8475	0·8717	0·8913	0·9074
0·7	0·4346	0·5239	0·5901	0·6419	0·6839	0·7180	0·7484	0·7738	0·7957
0·8	0·2994	0·3691	0·4235	0·4684	0·5065	0·5395	0·5687	0·5945	0·6181
0·9	0·1527	0·1921	0·2243	0·2518	0·2761	0·2977	0·3178	0·3357	0·3528

Table A. 8. THE CHANCE A CUSTOMER DOES NOT HAVE TO WAIT FOR SERVICE IN THE QUEUE $D/M/n$

Utilisation (u)	Number of Servers (n)								
	2	3	4	5	6	7	8	9	10
0·1	1·0000	1·0000	1·0000	1·0000	1·0000	1·0000	1·0000	1·0000	1·0000
0·2	0·9994	0·9999	1·0000	1·0000	1·0000	1·0000	1·0000	1·0000	1·0000
0·3	0·9908	0·9977	0·9994	0·9998	1·0000	1·0000	1·0000	1·0000	1·0000
0·4	0·9602	0·9838	0·9931	0·9970	0·9987	0·9994	0·9997	0·9999	0·9999
0·5	0·8966	0·9429	0·9672	0·9807	0·9884	0·9930	0·9957	0·9973	0·9983
0·6	0·7946	0·8611	0·9027	0·9304	0·9494	0·9628	0·9724	0·9794	0·9846
0·7	0·6528	0·7288	0·7826	0·8227	0·8536	0·8781	0·8978	0·9138	0·9270
0·8	0·4718	0·5416	0·5952	0·6385	0·6745	0·7051	0·7316	0·7547	0·7751
0·9	0·2535	0·2983	0·3348	0·3659	0·3932	0·4175	0·4394	0·4595	0·4780

Table A.9. THE CHANCE A CUSTOMER DOES NOT HAVE TO WAIT FOR SERVICE IN THE QUEUE $E_2/E_2/n$

Utilisation (u)	Number of Servers (n)								
	2	3	4	5	6	7	8	9	10
0·1	0·9983	0·9999	1·0000	1·0000	1·0000	1·0000	1·0000	1·0000	1·0000
0·2	0·9834	0·9961	0·9990	0·9998	0·9999	1·0000	1·0000	1·0000	1·0000
0·3	0·9456	0·9792	0·9916	0·9965	0·9985	0·9994	0·9997	0·9999	0·9999
0·4	0·8812	0·9386	0·9667	0·9814	0·9894	0·9939	0·9964	0·9979	0·9988
0·5	0·7903	0·8673	0·9125	0·9408	0·9593	0·9716	0·9800	0·9857	0·9898
0·6	0·6746	0·7622	0·8200	0·8610	0·8911	0·9138	0·9311	0·9446	0·9550
0·7	0·5355	0·6215	0·6840	0·7309	0·7702	0·8014	0·8272	0·8488	0·8673
0·8*	0·37	0·45	0·50	0·56	0·58	0·62	0·64	0·68	0·69
0·9*	0·19	0·25	0·26	0·31	0·32	0·36	0·36	0·40	0·40

* These figures in these rows were obtained by simulation.

Table A.10. THE AVERAGE BUSY PERIOD OF INDIVIDUAL SERVERS IN THE QUEUE $M/M/n$ IN UNITS OF AVERAGE SERVICE TIME

Utilisation (u)	Number of Servers (n)								
	2	3	4	5	6	7	8	9	10
0·1	1·0185	1·0037	1·0008	1·0002	1·0000	1·0000	1·0000	1·0000	1·0000
0·2	1·0714	1·0253	1·0097	1·0038	1·0016	1·0006	1·0003	1·0001	1·0000
0·3	1·1607	1·0753	1·0385	1·0206	1·0113	1·0063	1·0035	1·0020	1·0012
0·4	1·2963	1·1644	1·0997	1·0635	1·0416	1·0278	1·0188	1·0129	1·0089
0·5	1·5000	1·3103	1·2105	1·1499	1·1101	1·0825	1·0627	1·0483	1·0375
0·6	1·8182	1·5498	1·4026	1·3092	1·2447	1·1977	1·1622	1·1346	1·1127
0·7	2·3611	1·9698	1·7503	1·6073	1·5060	1·4301	1·3710	1·3237	1·2849
0·8	3·4615	2·8344	2·4779	2·2427	2·0737	1·9453	1·8438	1·7613	1·6926
0·9	6·7857	5·4663	4·7115	4·2104	3·8480	3·5709	3·3505	3·1699	3·0187

(The discipline first idle—first back in service is assumed)

Table A.11. AVERAGE WAITING TIME OF CUSTOMERS IN THE QUEUE $M/M/n$ WITH A LIMIT OF N ON THE QUEUE LENGTH

Utilisation* (u)	Limit on Queue size (N)	Number of Servers (n)								
		2	3	4	5	6	7	8	9	10
0·1	1	0·0082	0·0011	0·0002	0·0000					
	2	0·0098	0·0013	0·0002	0·0000					
	3	0·0101	0·0014	0·0002	0·0000					
	∞	0·0101	0·0014	0·0002	0·0000					
0·2	1	0·0267	0·0066	0·0019	0·0006	0·0002	0·0001			
	2	0·0374	0·0092	0·0027	0·0009	0·0003	0·0001			
	3	0·0405	0·0100	0·0029	0·0009	0·0003	0·0001			
	4	0·0414	0·0102	0·0030	0·0010	0·0003	0·0001			
	5	0·0416	0·0103	0·0030	0·0010	0·0003	0·0001			
	∞	0·0417	0·0103	0·0030	0·0010	0·0003	0·0001			
0·3	1	0·0491	0·0164	0·0065	0·0023	0·0013	0·0006	0·0003	0·0002	0·0001
	2	0·0778	0·0262	0·0104	0·0045	0·0021	0·0010	0·0005	0·0003	0·0001
	3	0·0907	0·0306	0·0121	0·0053	0·0024	0·0012	0·0006	0·0003	0·0002
	4	0·0959	0·0323	0·0128	0·0056	0·0026	0·0012	0·0006	0·0003	0·0002
	5	0·0978	0·0330	0·0131	0·0057	0·0026	0·0013	0·0006	0·0003	0·0002
	6	0·0985	0·0332	0·0132	0·0057	0·0026	0·0013	0·0006	0·0003	0·0002
	7	0·0988	0·0333	0·0132	0·0057	0·0027	0·0013	0·0006	0·0003	0·0002
	8	0·0989	0·0333	0·0132	0·0058	0·0027	0·0013	0·0006	0·0003	0·0002
	∞	0·0989	0·0333	0·0132	0·0058	0·0027	0·0013	0·0006	0·0003	0·0002
0·4	1	0·0712	0·0289	0·0138	0·0072	0·0040	0·0023	0·0014	0·0009	0·0005
	2	0·1253	0·0513	0·0246	0·0129	0·0072	0·0042	0·0025	0·0015	0·0010

Table A.11. (continued)

Utilisation* (u)	Limit on Queue size (N)	Number of Servers (n)								
		2	3	4	5	6	7	8	9	10
	3	0·1573	0·0646	0·0311	0·0164	0·0091	0·0053	0·0032	0·0019	0·0012
	4	0·1743	0·0717	0·0345	0·0182	0·0101	0·0059	0·0035	0·0022	0·0013
	5	0·1828	0·0753	0·0363	0·0191	0·0106	0·0062	0·0037	0·0023	0·0014
	6	0·1870	0·0770	0·0371	0·0195	0·0109	0·0063	0·0038	0·0023	0·0014
	7	0·1889	0·0778	0·0375	0·0197	0·0110	0·0064	0·0038	0·0023	0·0015
	8	0·1898	0·0781	0·0376	0·0198	0·0111	0·0064	0·0038	0·0023	0·0015
	9	0·1902	0·0783	0·0377	0·0199	0·0111	0·0064	0·0038	0·0024	0·0015
	10	0·1903	0·0784	0·0378	0·0199	0·0111	0·0064	0·0039	0·0024	0·0015
	11	0·1904	0·0784	0·0378	0·0199	0·0111	0·0064	0·0039	0·0024	0·0015
	12	0·1905	0·0784	0·0378	0·0199	0·0111	0·0064	0·0039	0·0024	0·0015
	∞	0·1905	0·0784	0·0378	0·0199	0·0111	0·0064	0·0039	0·0024	0·0015
0·5	1	0·0909	0·0420	0·0227	0·0135	0·0085	0·0055	0·0037	0·0026	0·0018
	2	0·1739	0·0814	0·0444	0·0265	0·0167	0·0110	0·0074	0·0051	0·0036
	3	0·2340	0,1102	0·0604	0·0361	0·0229	0·0150	0·0102	0·0071	0·0050
	4	0·2737	0·1292	0·0710	0·0425	0·0269	0·0177	0·0120	0·0083	0·0059
	5	0·2984	0·1411	0·0777	0·0465	0·0295	0·0194	0·0132	0·0091	0·0064
	6	0·3133	0·1483	0·0816	0·0489	0·0310	0·0204	0·0138	0·0096	0·0068
	8	0·3270	0·1549	0·0853	0·0511	0·0324	0·0213	0·0145	0·0100	0·0071
	10	0·3314	0·1570	0·0865	0·0518	0·0329	0·0216	0·0147	0·0102	0·0072
	15	0·3332	0·1579	0·0869	0·0521	0·0330	0·0218	0·0148	0·0102	0·0072
	∞	0·3333	0·1579	0·0870	0·0521	0·0330	0·0218	0·0148	0·0102	0·0072

	n									
0·6	1	0·1074	0·0542	0·0320	0·0206	0·0141	0·0100	0·0073	0·0055	0·0042
	2	0·2193	0·1127	0·0673	0·0438	0·0301	0·0215	0·0158	0·0119	0·0091
	3	0·3135	0·1626	0·0978	0·0639	0·0441	0·0316	0·0233	0·0176	0·0135
	4	0·3865	0·2016	0·1217	0·0798	0·0551	0·0396	0·0292	0·0221	0·0169
	5	0·4405	0·2305	0·1394	0·0915	0·0634	0·0455	0·0337	0·0254	0·0195
	6	0·4793	0·2512	0·1522	0·1000	0·0693	0·0498	0·0368	0·0278	0·0214
	8	0·5252	0·2758	0·1672	0·1100	0·0763	0·0549	0·0406	0·0307	0·0236
	10	0·5464	0·2871	0·1742	0·1146	0·0795	0·0572	0·0423	0·0320	0·0246
	15	0·5607	0·2947	0·1788	0·1177	0·0816	0·0588	0·0435	0·0329	0·0252
	20	0·5623	0·2955	0·1793	0·1180	0·0819	0·0589	0·0436	0·0329	0·0253
	∞	0·5625	0·2956	0·1794	0·1181	0·0819	0·0589	0·0436	0·0329	0·0253
0·7	1	0·1205	0·0649	0·0407	0·0278	0·0201	0·0151	0·0117	0·0093	0·0075
	2	0·2587	0·1422	0·0905	0·0625	0·0456	0·0345	0·0268	0·0214	0·0173
	3	0·3884	0·2161	0·1387	0·0965	0·0707	0·0538	0·0420	0·0335	0·0272
	4	0·5019	0·2814	0·1816	0·1269	0·0933	0·0712	0·0557	0·0446	0·0362
	5	0·5976	0·3367	0·2181	0·1528	0·1127	0·0861	0·0675	0·0541	0·0440
	6	0·6764	0·3823	0·2483	0·1743	0·1287	0·0985	0·0773	0·0620	0·0505
	8	0·7909	0·4487	0·2923	0·2057	0·1521	0·1166	0·0917	0·0735	0·0600
	10	0·8621	0·4900	0·3196	0·2251	0·1667	0·1278	0·1005	0·0807	0·0658
	15	0·9375	0·5336	0·3484	0·2456	0·1820	0·1396	0·1099	0·0883	0·0720
	20	0·9557	0·5441	0·3553	0·2505	0·1856	0·1424	0·1121	0·0901	0·0735
	25	0·9597	0·5465	0·3568	0·2516	0·1864	0·1431	0·1126	0·0905	0·0738
	30	0·9606	0·5469	0·3571	0·2518	0·1866	0·1432	0·1127	0·0905	0·0739
	∞	0·9607	0·5470	0·3572	0·2519	0·1866	0·1432	0·1127	0·0906	0·0739
0·8	1	0·1305	0·0737	0·0482	0·0343	0·0258	0·0202	0·0162	0·0133	0·0111
	2	0·2907	0·1678	0·1116	0·0805	0·0611	0·0481	0·0389	0·0321	0·0269
	3	0·4535	0·2654	0·1784	0·1296	0·0990	0·0784	0·0636	0·0528	0·0444
	4	0·6090	0·3597	0·2434	0·1779	0·1365	0·1085	0·0884	0·0735	0·0621

Table A.11.*(continued)

173

Utilisation* (u)	Limit on Queue size (N)	Number of Servers (n)								
		2	3	4	5	6	7	8	9	10
	5	0·7531	0·4477	0·3046	0·2234	0·1721	0·1371	0·1120	0·0933	0·0790
	6	0·8844	0·5283	0·3607	0·2654	0·2049	0·1636	0·1339	0·1118	0·0947
	8	1·1081	0·6660	0·4569	0·3375	0·2614	0·2093	0·1718	0·1437	0·1220
	10	1·2835	0·7742	0·5327	0·3944	0·3061	0·2455	0·2018	0·1691	0·1437
	15	1·5588	0·9440	0·6516	0·4837	0·3762	0·3024	0·2490	0·2089	0·1778
	20	1·6864	1·0226	0·7064	0·5249	0·4086	0·3286	0·2707	0·2272	0·1935
	25	1·7412	1·0563	0·7300	0·5425	0·4224	0·3397	0·2799	0·2350	0·2002
	30	1·7636	1·0700	0·7395	0·5496	0·4280	0·3443	0·2837	0·2381	0·2029
	35	1·7724	1·0754	0·7433	0·5524	0·4301	0·3460	0·2851	0·2394	0·2040
	40	1·7758	1·0774	0·7447	0·5535	0·4310	0·3467	0·2857	0·2398	0·204(
	45	1·7770	1·0782	0·7452	0·5539	0·4313	0·3470	0·2859	0·2400	0·2045
	50	1·7775	1·0785	0·7454	0·5540	0·4314	0·3470	0·2860	0·2401	0·2046
	∞	1·7776	1·0785	0·7455	0·5541	0·4314	0·3471	0·2860	0·2401	0·2046
0·9	1	0·1378	0·0805	0·0544	0·0399	0·0308	0·0247	0·0203	0·0171	0·0146
	2	0·3154	0·1886	0·1295	0·0961	0·0750	0·0606	0·0503	0·0425	0·0365
	3	0·5061	0·3070	0·2132	0·1596	0·1254	0·1019	0·0850	0·0722	0·0623
	4	0·6994	0·4287	0·3000	0·2260	0·1785	0·1457	0·1220	0·1040	0·0900
	5	0·8907	0·5500	0·3871	0·2930	0·2323	0·1904	0·1598	0·1366	0·1185
	6	1·0776	0·6692	0·4730	0·3593	0·2858	0·2348	0·1976	0·1693	0·1472
	8	1·4334	0·8973	0·6382	0·4873	0·3894	0·3212	0·2711	0·2331	0·2032
	10	1·7615	1·1085	0·7917	0·6067	0·4863	0·4021	0·3403	0·2932	0·2561

15	2·4570	1·5575	1·1190	0·8618	0·6938	0·5759	0·4891	0·4227	0·3704
20	2·9869	1·9000	1·3691	1·0570	0·8527	0·7093	0·6034	0·5223	0·4584
25	3·3871	2·1529	1·5536	1·2010	0·9700	0·8077	0·6878	0·5958	0·5233
30	3·6593	2·3345	1·6861	1·3043	1·0541	0·8782	0·7482	0·6486	0·5699
40	3·9934	2·5500	1·8432	1·4268	1·1537	0·9617	0·8198	0·7109	0·6249
50	4·1477	2·6494	1·9155	1·4831	1·1995	1·0000	0·8526	0·7394	0·6501
60	4·2153	2·6928	1·9471	1·5077	1·2195	1·0168	0·8669	0·7519	0·6610
70	4·2438	2·7111	1·9604	1·5180	1·2279	1·0238	0·8729	0·7571	0·6651
80	4·2555	2·7186	1·9658	1·5222	1·2313	1·0266	0·8753	0·7592	0·6669
90	4·2602	2·7216	1·9680	1·5239	1·2327	1·0278	0·8763	0·7601	0·6677
100	4·2620	2·7228	1·9688	1·5246	1·2332	1·0282	0·8767	0·7604	0·6679
∞	4·2627	2·7232	1·9692	1·5248	1·2334	1·0284	0·8768	0·7605	0·6680

* In these tables the utilisation, u, is that of the system before customers are turned away. The actual utilisation is given by:

Actual Utilisation $= (1 - P)u$

$P =$ the chance a customer is turned away

Table A.12. THE CHANCE A CUSTOMER IS TURNED AWAY, P, IN THE QUEUE $M/M/n$ WITH A LIMIT OF N ON THE QUEUE LENGTH

Utilisation* (u)	Limit on Queue size (N)	Number of Servers (n)								
		2	3	4	5	6	7	8	9	10
0·1	1	0·0016	0·0003	0·0001						
	2	0·0002	0·0000	0·0000						
	3	0·0000	0·0000	0·0000						
0·2	1	0·0107	0·0039	0·0015	0·0006	0·0003	0·0001			
	2	0·0021	0·0008	0·0003	0·0001	0·0001	0·0000			
	3	0·0004	0·0002	0·0001	0·0000	0·0000	0·0000			
	4	0·0001	0·0000	0·0000	0·0000	0·0000	0·0000			
	5	0·0000	0·0000	0·0000	0·0000	0·0000	0·0000			
0·3	1	0·0294	0·0148	0·0078	0·0042	0·0023	0·0013	0·0007	0·0004	0·0002
	2	0·0088	0·0044	0·0023	0·0013	0·0007	0·0004	0·0002	0·0001	0·0001
	3	0·0026	0·0013	0·0007	0·0004	0·0002	0·0001	0·0001	0·0000	0·0000
	4	0·0008	0·0004	0·0002	0·0001	0·0001	0·0000	0·0000	0·0000	0·0000
	5	0·0002	0·0001	0·0001	0·0000	0·0000	0·0000	0·0000	0·0000	0·0000
	6	0·0001	0·0000	0·0000	0·0000	0·0000	0·0000	0·0000	0·0000	0·0000
	7	0·0000	0·0000	0·0000	0·0000	0·0000	0·0000	0·0000	0·0000	0·0000
0·4	1	0·0569	0·0347	0·0221	0·0145	0·0097	0·0065	0·0045	0·0031	0·0021
	2	0·0223	0·0137	0·0088	0·0058	0·0038	0·0026	0·0018	0·0012	0·0008
	3	0·0088	0·0054	0·0035	0·0023	0·0015	0·0010	0·0007	0·0005	0·0003
	4	0·0035	0·0022	0·0014	0·0009	0·0006	0·0004	0·0003	0·0002	0·0001
	5	0·0014	0·0009	0·0006	0·0004	0·0002	0·0002	0·0001	0·0001	0·0001
	6	0·0006	0·0003	0·0002	0·0001	0·0001	0·0001	0·0000	0·0000	0·0000

p	n									
0·5	7	0·0000	0·0000	0·0000	0·0000	0·0000	0·0001	0·0001	0·0001	0·0002
	8	0·0000	0·0000	0·0000	0·0000	0·0000	0·0000	0·0000	0·0001	0·0001
	9	0·0000	0·0000	0·0000	0·0000	0·0000	0·0000	0·0000	0·0000	0·0000
0·6	1	0·0091	0·0116	0·0150	0·0194	0·0254	0·0337	0·0455	0·0629	0·0909
	2	0·0045	0·0058	0·0074	0·0096	0·0125	0·0166	0·0222	0·0305	0·0435
	3	0·0023	0·0029	0·0037	0·0048	0·0062	0·0082	0·0110	0·0150	0·0213
	4	0·0011	0·0014	0·0018	0·0024	0·0031	0·0041	0·0055	0·0075	0·0105
	5	0·0006	0·0007	0·0009	0·0012	0·0016	0·0020	0·0027	0·0037	0·0052
	6	0·0003	0·0004	0·0005	0·0006	0·0008	0·0010	0·0014	0·0019	0·0026
	8	0·0001	0·0001	0·0001	0·0001	0·0002	0·0003	0·0003	0·0005	0·0007
	10	0·0000	0·0000	0·0000	0·0000	0·0000	0·0001	0·0001	0·0001	0·0002
	12	0·0000	0·0000	0·0000	0·0000	0·0000	0·0000	0·0000	0·0000	0·0000
0·7	1	0·0252	0·0297	0·0353	0·0421	0·0508	0·0619	0·0768	0·0976	0·1289
	2	0·0149	0·0175	0·0207	0·0246	0·0296	0·0358	0·0441	0·0553	0·0718
	3	0·0089	0·0104	0·0123	0·0146	0·0174	0·0210	0·0258	0·0321	0·0413
	4	0·0053	0·0062	0·0073	0·0087	0·0103	0·0125	0·0152	0·0189	0·0242
	5	0·0032	0·0037	0·0044	0·0052	0·0062	0·0074	0·0090	0·0112	0·0143
	6	0·0019	0·0022	0·0026	0·0031	0·0037	0·0044	0·0054	0·0067	0·0085
	8	0·0007	0·0008	0·0009	0·0011	0·0013	0·0016	0·0019	0·0024	0·0030
	10	0·0002	0·0003	0·0003	0·0004	0·0005	0·0006	0·0007	0·0009	0·0010
	15	0·0000	0·0000	0·0000	0·0000	0·0000	0·0000	0·0001	0·0001	0·0001
	20	0·0000	0·0000	0·0000	0·0000	0·0000	0·0000	0·0000	0·0000	0·0000
	1	0·0522	0·0583	0·0655	0·0741	0·0845	0·0974	0·1140	0·1363	0·1687
	2	0·0353	0·0392	0·0438	0·0493	0·0558	0·0638	0·0739	0·0871	0·1056
	3	0·0241	0·0267	0·0298	0·0334	0·0376	0·0428	0·0492	0·0575	0·0688
	4	0·0166	0·0184	0·0204	0·0228	0·0256	0·0291	0·0333	0·0387	0·0460
	5	0·0115	0·0127	0·0141	0·0157	0·0176	0·0199	0·0228	0·0264	0·0312
	6	0·0080	0·0088	0·0098	0·0109	0·0122	0·0138	0·0157	0·0181	0·0214

Table A.12. (continued)

Utilisation* (u)	Limit on Queue (N)	Number of Servers (n)								
		2	3	4	5	6	7	8	9	10
	8	0·0102	0·0087	0·0075	0·0066	0·0059	0·0053	0·0047	0·0043	0·0039
	10	0·0049	0·0042	0·0036	0·0032	0·0029	0·0026	0·0023	0·0021	0·0019
	15	0·0008	0·0007	0·0006	0·0005	0·0005	0·0004	0·0004	0·0003	0·0003
	20	0·0001	0·0001	0·0001	0·0001	0·0001	0·0001	0·0001	0·0001	0·0001
	25	0·0000	0·0000	0·0000	0·0000	0·0000	0·0000	0·0000	0·0000	0·0000
0·8	1	0·2088	0·1768	0·1543	0·1374	0·1239	0·1128	0·1036	0·0956	0·0887
	2	0·1431	0·1239	0·1099	0·0990	0·0902	0·0828	0·0765	0·0710	0·0663
	3	0·1027	0·0902	0·0808	0·0734	0·0673	0·0621	0·0577	0·0538	0·0503
	4	0·0760	0·0673	0·0607	0·0555	0·0511	0·0473	0·0441	0·0413	0·0387
	5	0·0573	0·0511	0·0463	0·0425	0·0393	0·0365	0·0341	0·0319	0·0300
	6	0·0438	0·0393	0·0357	0·0329	0·0305	0·0284	0·0265	0·0249	0·0235
	8	0·0264	0·0238	0·0218	0·0201	0·0187	0·0174	0·0164	0·0154	0·0145
	10	0·0163	0·0147	0·0135	0·0125	0·0116	0·0109	0·0102	0·0096	0·0091
	15	0·0051	0·0046	0·0043	0·0040	0·0037	0·0035	0·0033	0·0031	0·0029
	20	0·0017	0·0015	0·0014	0·0013	0·0012	0·0011	0·0011	0·0010	0·0009
	25	0·0005	0·0005	0·0005	0·0004	0·0004	0·0004	0·0003	0·0003	0·0003
	30	0·0002	0·0002	0·0001	0·0001	0·0001	0·0001	0·0001	0·0001	0·0001
	35	0·0001	0·0001	0·0000	0·0000	0·0000	0·0000	0·0000	0·0000	0·0000
	40	0·0000	0·0000	0·0000	0·0000	0·0000	0·0000	0·0000	0·0000	0·0000
0·9	1	0·2480	0·2174	0·1959	0·1795	0·1663	0·1554	0·1462	0·1383	0·1313
	2	0·1825	0·1637	0·1499	0·1391	0·1302	0·1227	0·1163	0·1107	0·1057

3	0·1411	0·1284	0·1189	0·1112	0·1049	0·0995	0·0948	0·0906	0·0869
4	0·1127	0·1036	0·0966	0·0910	0·0863	0·0822	0·0786	0·0754	0·0725
5	0·0921	0·0853	0·0800	0·0757	0·0720	0·0689	0·0661	0·0635	0·0613
6	0·0765	0·0713	0·0672	0·0638	0·0609	0·0584	0·0561	0·0541	0·0523
8	0·0548	0·0515	0·0488	0·0466	0·0447	0·0430	0·0415	0·0401	0·0389
10	0·0406	0·0383	0·0365	0·0349	0·0336	0·0324	0·0314	0·0304	0·0295
15	0·0208	0·0198	0·0190	0·0183	0·0177	0·0171	0·0166	0·0161	0·0157
20	0·0114	0·0109	0·0105	0·0101	0·0098	0·0095	0·0092	0·0090	0·0088
25	0·0065	0·0062	0·0060	0·0058	0·0056	0·0054	0·0053	0·0051	0·0050
30	0·0037	0·0036	0·0034	0·0033	0·0032	0·0031	0·0031	0·0030	0·0029
40	0·0013	0·0012	0·0012	0·0011	0·0011	0·0011	0·0010	0·0010	0·0010
50	0·0004	0·0004	0·0004	0·0004	0·0004	0·0004	0·0004	0·0004	0·0003
60	0·0002	0·0001	0·0001	0·0001	0·0001	0·0001	0·0001	0·0001	0·0001
70	0·0001	0·0001	0·0000	0·0000	0·0000	0·0000	0·0000	0·0000	0·0000
80	0·0000	0·0000	0·0000	0·0000	0·0000	0·0000	0·0000	0·0000	0·0000

* In these tables the utilisation is that of the system before customers are turned away. The actual utilisation is given by:

Actual utilisation $= (1-P) \times$ average service time/(n $\times$ average arrival interval)

where P = the proportion of customers turned away.

i.e. Actual utilisation $= (1-P) \times$ utilisation without customers turned away.

$= (1-P)u$

Glossary

a = Average arrival interval = $1/\lambda$

$\bar{B}$ = Average busy period of service system.

c.v. = Coefficient of variation of a distribution = standard deviation/mean.

D = Notation for the deterministic or constant distribution in Kendall's description of a queueing system.

E_k = Notation for the Erlang distribution in Kendall's description of a queueing system.

The Erlang distribution with average a and (c.v.)^2 = k^{-1} has a probability density function $f(t) = (k/a)^k t^{k-1} e^{-kt/a}/(k-1)!$

G = Notation for a general form of distribution in Kendall's description of a queueing system.

$\bar{I}$ = The average idle period of the service system.

L = The average number of customers in the queue.

m = The number of operatives in machine interference problems.

M = Notation for the negative exponential distribution in Kendall's description of a queueing system.

The negative exponential distribution with average a has a probability density function $f(t) = \dfrac{1}{a} e^{-t/a}$

n = The number of servers in the system.

N = The limit on queue size in finite queues.

$P_t(j)$ = The probability of there being j customers in the system at time t.

$P(j)$ = The probability of there being j customers in the system in the steady state.

s = The average service time of a customer = $1/\mu$.

u = The utilisation of the system.

v_a = Variability of inter arrival distribution = (c.v.)^2 of arrivals.

v_s = Variability of service time distribution = (c.v.)^2 of service time.

$W(t)$ = Distribution of customer waiting time, t.

W = Average waiting time of all customers.

λ = Arrival rate of customers.

μ = Service rate of individual servers.

ϱ = The traffic intensity or number of customers arriving per service time = $= \lambda/\mu$

References

1. KENDALL, D. G. 'Stochastic Processes Occurring in the Theory of Queues and their Analysis by the Method of the imbedded Markov Chain', *Ann. Math. Stat.*, **24**, 338–354, (1953).
2. HOEL, P. G., *Introduction to Statistics*, Wiley (1947).
3. WEATHERBURN, C. E., *A First Course in Mathematical Statistics*, Cambridge University Press (1961).
4. COX, D. R. and SMITH, W. L., *Queues*, Methuen (1961)
5. PHILLIPS, E. G., *A Course of Analysis*, Cambridge University Press (1950).
6. TANNER, J. C., 'A derivation of the Borel Distribution', *Biometrika*, **48**, 222 (1961)
7. BOREL, E., 'Sur l'emploi due théorème de Bernouilli pour faciliter le calcul d'une infinité de coefficients', *Comptes Rendus Acad. Sci. Paris*, **214**, 452 (1942).
8. PRABHU, N. U., *Queues and Inventories*, Wiley (1965).
9. SHELTON, J. R., 'Solution Methods for Waiting Line Problems', *J. Industr. Eng.*, **II**, no. 4, (1960).
10. LITTLE, J. D. C., 'A Proof for the Queueing Formula $L = \lambda W$', *Opns. Res.*, **9**, 383–387 (1961).
11. JEWELL, W. S., 'A simple proof of: $L = \lambda W$', *Opns. Res.*, **15**, 1109–1116 (1967).
12. EILON, S., 'A simple proof of $L = \lambda W$', *Opns. Res.*, **17**, 915–917 (1969).
13. ELDERTON, SIR W., *Frequency Curves and Correlation*.
14. KENDALL, D. G., 'Some Problems in the Theory of Queues', *J. Roy. Stat. Soc.*, (B), **13**, no. 2, 151–173 (1951).
15. MAYHUGH, J. O. and MCCORMICK, R. E., 'Steady State Solution of the Queue $M/E_k/r$', *Management Science*, **14**, no. 11, 692–712 (1968).
16. FELLER, W., *An Introduction to Probability Theory and its Applications*, Vol. 1., Wiley (1968).
17. BENSON, F. and COX, D. R., 'The Productivity of Machines requiring attention at Random Intervals', *J. Roy. Stat. Soc.*, (B), **13**, 65 (1951).
18. COX, D. R., 'A Table for predicting the Production of a Group of Machines under the care of one Operative', *J. Roy. Stat. Soc.*, (B), **16**, 285 (1954).

182   References

19. ASHCROFT, H., 'The Productivity of several Machines under the care of one Operator', *J. Roy. Stat. Soc.*, (B), 12, no. 1, 145–151 (1950).
20. ANSON, C., J., 'Determining Machine and Operator utilisation and Synchronisation Allowances', *Time and Motion Study*, 5, 15 (1956).
21. BENSON, F., *Machine Interference*, Ph. D. Thesis, University of Birmingham (1957).
22. COX, D. R., 'Prévision de la Production d'un Groupe de Machines surveillées par un Exécutant', *Les Cahiers du B.T.E.*, No. 503–02 (1955).
23. PECK, L. G. and HAZELWOOD, R. N., *Finite Queueing Tables*, Wiley (1958).
24. HAIGHT, F. A., 'Queueing with Balking', *Biometrika*, 44, nos 3 and 4, 360 (1957).
25. HAIGHT, F. A., 'Queueing with Balking—II', *Biometrika*, 47, nos 3 and 4, 285 (1960).
26. FINCH, P. D., 'Deterministic customer impatience in the Queueing System GI/M/1', *Biometrika*, 47, nos 1 and 2, 45 (1960).
27. GHOSAL, A., 'Queues with finite waiting time', *Opns. Res.*, 11, no. 6, 919 (1963).
28. ANCKER, C. J. JNR., and GAFARIAN, A. V., 'Some Queueing Problems with balking and reneging', *Opns. Res.*, 11, no. 1, 88 (1963).
29. ANCKER, C. J. JNR., and GAFARIAN, A. V., 'Some Queueing Problems with balking and reneging—II', *Opns. Res.*, 11, no. 6, 928 (1963).
30. RAO, S. S., 'Queueing Models with balking, reneging and interruptions', *Opns. Res.*, 13, no. 4, 596 (1965).
31. RAO, S. S. and JAISWAL, N. K., 'On a class of Queueing Problems and Discrete Transforms', *Opns. Res.*, 17, no. 6, 1062–76 (1969).
32. DALEY, D. J., 'General Customer Impatience in the Queue G1/G/1', *J. Appl. Probab.* 2, no. 1, 186 (1965).
33. SINGH, V. P., 'Two Server Markovian Queues with balking: Heterogeneous vs. Homogeneous Servers', *Opns. Res.*, 18, no. 1, 145–159 (1970).
34. MORSE, P. M., *Queues, Inventories and Maintenance*, Wiley, (1958).
35. JAISWAL, N. K., *Priority Queues*, Academic Press (1968).
36. COBHAM, A., 'Priority Assignment in Waiting Line Problems', *Opns. Res.*, 2, 70–76 (1954).
37. OLIVER, R. M. and PESTALOZZI, G., 'On a Problem of Optimum Priority Classification', *J. Soc. Indust. Appl. Math.*, 13, no. 3, 890–901 (1965).
38. KESTEN, H. and RUNNENBURG, J. T., 'Priority in Waiting Line Problems', *Koninklijke Nederlandse Akademie van Wetenschappen*, 60, No. 3, 312–336 (1957).
39. BROSH, I., 'Pre-emptive Priority Assignment in Multi Channel Systems', *Opns. Res.*, 17, no. 3, 526–535 (1969).
40. SEGAL, M., 'A Multiserver Queue with pre-emptive Priorities', *Opns. Res.*, 17, no. 3, 526–535 (1969)
41. ADIRI, I., and AVI ITZHAK B., 'A Time Sharing Queue', *Mgmt. Sci.*, 15, no. 11, 639–657 (1969)
42. ADIRI, I., and AVI ITZHAK B., 'A Time Sharing Model with many Queues', *Opns. Res.*, 17, no. 6, 1077–1089 (1969)
43. SCHRAGE, L., 'A Mixed Priority Queue with applications to the Analysis of Real Time Systems', *Opns. Res.*, 17, no. 4, 728–742 (1969)
44. CHANG, W., 'Queueing Analysis of Real Time Computer Processing', *Mgmt. Sci.*, 15, no. 11, 658–671 (1969)

Solutions to Problems

Chapter 2

1. 6 berths
2. 1 server
3. 4 mechanics
4. Proportion leaving without a customer = $\frac{1}{3}$; Average wait = 4 min
5. No answer required
6. Average waiting time = 2·65 min; Reduction in waiting time = 1·94 min
7. 17 servers

Chapter 3

1. 96%
2. 20 h
3. 6 servers
4. 5 ships

Chapter 4

1. 9 containers
2. 7 min
3. No servers can be released

Chapter 5

1. 7 berths
2. 1·3 min, 1 extra truck
3. 6 h
4. First system

Chapter 6

1. $P(j)$ = chance j machines are running
   $P(0) = 0·1389$; $P(1) = P(2) = 0·2779$; $P(3) = 0·1852$; $P(4) = 0·0926$;
   $P(5) = 0·0247$; $P(6) = 0·0027$. Most likely number of machines in
   use is 1 or 2. Average number in use = 1·90
2. Average number running drops from 3·64 to 3·38 machines
3. 65·9% and 60·4%
4. 2 operatives
5.
Year	Expected Production
1970	390·6
1971	399·2
1972	477·8
1973	477·8
1974	555·1

Chapter 7

1. 81%, 20%
2. 42
3. 8
4. 9·5%, 7

Index